AUTO-BIOGRAPH

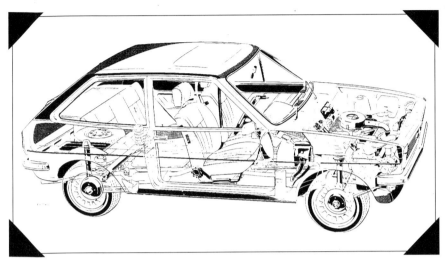

This page enables you to compile a list of useful data on your car, so that whether you're ordering spares or just checking the tyre pressures, all the key information - the information that is 'personal' to your car - is easily within reach.

Registration number: ....

Model: ....

Body colour: ....

Paint code number: ....

Date of first registration: ....,

Date of manufacture (if different): ....

Chassis or 'VIN' number: ....

Engine number: ....

Ignition key number: ....

Door lock key/keys number: ....

Fuel locking cap key number (if fitted): ....

Alarm remote code (if fitted): ....

Alarm remote battery type: ....

Radio/cassette security code (if fitted): ....

Tyre size

    Front: ....Rear:.................................

Tyre pressure (normally laden)

    Front: ....Rear:.................................

Tyre pressure (fully laden)

    Front: ....Rear:.................................

Insurance

    Name and address of insurer:...

    ....

    Policy number:...

Modifications

    Information that might be useful when you need to purchase parts:.......................................

    ....

    ....

Suppliers

    Address and telephone number of your garage and parts suppliers:......................................

    ....

First published in 1995 by Porter Publishing Ltd

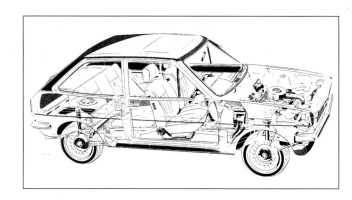

PORTER
PUBLISHING

The Storehouse
Little Hereford Street
Bromyard
Hereford HR7 4DE
England

British Library Cataloguing in Publication Data
A catalogue record for this book is available from the British Library

Series Editor: Lindsay Porter
Design: Lindsay Porter, and Lyndsay Berryman, Pineapple Publishing
Printed in England by The Trinity Press, Worcester

Every care has been taken to ensure that the material contained in this Service Guide is correct. However, no liability can be accepted by the authors or publishers for damage, loss, accidents, or injury resulting from any omissions or errors in the information given.

Other Titles in this Series
Caravan Owner's Manual & Service Guide
Classic 'Bike Service Guide
Land Rover Series I, II, III Service Guide
Land Rover Defender, 90 & 110 Service Guide
Mini (all models 1959-1994) Service Guide
MGB (including MGC, MGB GT V8 and MG RV8) Service Guide
MG Midget & Austin Healey Sprite Service Guide
VW Beetle Service Guide

- With more titles in production -

Absolute Beginners

Step-by-Step Service Guide

by Lindsay Porter and Denis Rea

FOREWORD

Despite the onslaught of the electronic age and its impact upon our working and leisure habits, nothing has yet usurped the convenience of a good book when it comes to looking after our four-wheeled "pride and joy". This book is no exception to that important rule.

Ironically, Castrol first developed a working relationship with Lindsay Porter, publisher of this book, some years ago when he launched a series of excellent videos about the classic motor racing of the 1950's and 60's. His idea was a practical solution to the challenge of getting the sense of excitement, accessibility and friendliness of motor racing, so typical of that period, into homes for the family to enjoy. That period happened to be one of the high points in the illustrious racing and record breaking heritage of Castrol. It was then that the Rover Group predecessor's products, notably the Mini, was winning all over the World with Castrol playing an important part in those successes. It continues today with the support of a number of Land Rover owners' expeditions into the World's most inhospitable places.

However, it was not those connections alone that encourage Castrol to support this publication. Denis Rea, the joint author, was for many years the editor of Practical Motorist. During his stewardship the magazine grew into D.I.Y. motorists'

favourite publication, primarily for the clarity it brought to the most challenging of tasks that D.I.Y. motorists contemplated taking on. The lively style drew the most timorous would-be weekend mechanics into the fold, initially, tackling simple tasks, with many readers moving on to seriously complex jobs. So be assured that you are in a safe pair of hands when you take Denis's advice.

I mentioned earlier the impact of the electronic age on our various lives. None more so than daily motoring. Without the car's electronic brain, the so-called "ECU", it would be less economic, far more polluting and probably none too smooth in its progress, assuming it started in the morning! All this sophistication may have lead some motorists to the view that "all that gubbins under the bonnet" is best left to the professional expert. Well this may be best for the "ECU" and fuel injection systems. But the other servicing functions are little changed and are still well within the scope of anyone with a modicum of practical bent. So don't be put off and try to take comfort from Denis Rea's safe advice - so long as you use Castrol oil, you understand!

Good luck with your next project be it your first or your umpteenth.

Richard Price
Manager, External Affairs
Castrol UK

CONTENTS

Lindsay Porter
M.D. Porter Publishing Ltd

Introduction

Over the years, I have run any number of cars, from superb classic cars, modern cars, to those with one foot in the breakers yard. And I know only too well that any car is only enjoyable to own if it's reliable, safe and basically sound - and the only way of ensuring that it stays that way is to service it regularly. That's why we have set about creating this book, which aims to show the newcomer to DIY car servicing that there's nothing to fear; you really *can* do it yourself!

Porter Publishing Service Guides are the first books to give you all the service information you might need, with step-by-step instructions, along with a complete Service History section for you to complete and fill in as you carry out regular maintenance on your car over the months ahead. Using the information contained in this book, you will be able to:

◆ see for yourself how to carry out every Service Interval, from weekly and monthly checks, right up to longer-term maintenance items.

◆ carry out regular body maintenance and rustproofing, saving a fortune in body repairs over the years to come.

◆ enhance the value of your car by completing a full Service History of every maintenance job you carry out on your car.

I hope you enjoy keeping your car in trim whilst saving lots of money by servicing your car yourself, with the help of this book. Happy motoring!

Lindsay Porter
Bromyard, Herefordshire

With ever more sophistication embodied in the humblest of family cars these days, there has been growing pressure from the motor trade to deter DIY and convince the new car buying public that only the dealer workshops (they need the money, of course!) can cope with their servicing requirements.

True, there is much electronic gadgetry that is beyond our comprehension, let alone our ability to service it! But note that even the trained professionals will make no effort to service or repair such equipment. Replacement is their only answer to faulty items, and expensive replacement at that - but more of this anon.

Meanwhile, there are, of course, still plenty of older or less sophisticated cars around whose servicing requirements are certainly within the scope of the DIY enthusiast. And if your car is new, once it is out of warranty, and you are no longer shackled to the dealer, remember this: there are still many aspects of even the most modern motor car that remain much the same as those of older design. And so there are still a significant number of servicing jobs that the DIY driver can tackle, as well as general care and attention.

And so, too, there is still much scope for saving money, not just on labour charges, but also on replacement parts - your engine oil and oil filter are just two typical examples of where prices will be markedly lower in High Street auto accessory shops, or out-of-town 'sheds', than those charged by the dealer workshops.

Not that it is all about saving money. Pride allied with competence is a powerful partnership. Over the many years that I have been looking after old and new cars of my own, and writing and broadcasting on the subject, I have become firmly convinced that given the necessary information (and it's all here in this book!) the dedicated DIY motorist can be just as competent, perhaps more so, than the average garage mechanic.

Add together the pride, the competence, and the enthusiasm one has for one's own vehicle, and you have the recipe for a thoroughly well looked after car - enjoyable to drive, safe, reliable, economical, better than average!

Denis Rea
Ringwood, Hampshire

Denis Rea

Thanks to John Bishop of Bishop's Garage, Bromyard for the loan of the car on the front cover.

Using This Book

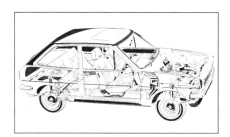

Everything about this book is designed to help you make your car more reliable and long-lasting through regular servicing. But one requirement that you will see emphasised again and again is the need for safe working. There is a lot of safety information within the practical instructions, but you are strongly urged to *read and take note of Chapter 1, Safety First!*

To get the most from this book, you will rapidly realise that it revolves around two main chapters. *Chapter 5, Service Intervals, Step-by-Step* shows you how to carry out every service job that your car is likely to need throughout its life. Then, the final Section, *Service History*, at the back of this book, lists all of the jobs described in *Chapter 5*, and arranges them together in tick-lists, a separate list for each Service interval, so that you can create your own *Service History* as you go along.

Keeping your car in top condition is one thing; getting it there in the first place may be quite another. At the start of *Chapter 5*, we advise on carrying out a 'catch-up' service for cars that may not have received the de-luxe treatment suggested here. And then there are other chapters to help you bring your car up to scratch. *Chapter 6, Repairing Bodywork Blemishes* shows how to make the body beautiful and how to keep it that way - not something that is usually included in servicing information but bodywork servicing can save you even more money than mechanical servicing, since a corroded body often leads to a scrapped car, whereas worn out mechanical components can usually be replaced. *Chapter 7* shows you how to carry out *Fault Finding* when your car won't start, and *Chapter 8* describes *Getting Through the MoT*, an annual worry - unless you follow the approach shown here. With *Chapter 2, Buying Spares* describing how you can save on spares, we hope that this book will become the first tool you'll pick up when you want to service your car!

This book is produced in association with Castrol (U.K.) Ltd.

"Cars have become more and more sophistated. But changing the oil and brake fluid, and similar jobs are as simple as they ever were. Castrol are pleased to be associated with this book because it gives us the opportunity to make life simpler for those who wish to service their own cars.
Castrol have succeeded in making oil friendlier and kinder to the environment by removing harmful chlorine from our range of engine lubricants which in turn prolong the life of the catalytic convertor (when fitted), by noticeably maintaining the engine at peak efficiency.
In return, we ask you to be kinder to the environment too... by taking yor used oil to your Local Authority Amenity Oil Bank. It can then be used as a heating fuel. Please do not poison it with thinners, paint, creosote or brake fluid because these render it useless and costly to dispose of."

Castrol (U.K.) Ltd

CHAPTER 1 - SAFETY FIRST!

It is vitally important that you always take time to ensure that safety is the first consideration in any job you do. A slight lack of concentration, or a rush to finish the job quickly can often result in an accident, as can failure to follow a few simple precautions. Whereas skilled motor mechanics are trained in safe working practices you, the home mechanic, must find them out for yourself and act upon them.

Remember, accidents don't just happen, they are caused, and some of those causes are contained in the following list. Above all, ensure that whenever you work on your car you adopt a safety-minded approach at all times, and remain aware of the dangers that might be encountered.

Be sure to consult the suppliers of any materials and equipment you may use, and to obtain and read carefully any operating and health and safety instructions that may be available on packaging or from manufacturers and suppliers.

IMPORTANT POINTS

ALWAYS ensure that the vehicle is properly supported when raised off the ground. Don't work on, around, or underneath a raised vehicle unless axle stands are positioned under secure, load bearing underbody areas, or the vehicle is driven onto ramps.

DON'T suddenly remove the radiator or expansion tank filler cap when the cooling system is hot, or you may get scalded by escaping coolant. Let the system cool down first and even then, if the engine is not completely cold, cover the cap with a cloth and gradually release the pressure.

NEVER start the engine unless the gearbox is in neutral (or 'Park' in the case of automatic transmission) and the hand brake is fully applied.

NEVER drain oil, coolant or automatic transmission fluid when the engine is hot. Allow time for it to cool sufficiently to avoid scalding you.

TAKE CARE when parking vehicles fitted with catalytic converters. The `cat' reaches extremely high temperatures and any combustible materials under the car, such as long dry grass, could ignite.

NEVER run catalytic converter equipped vehicles without the exhaust system heat shields in place.

NEVER attempt to loosen or tighten nuts that require a lot of force to turn (e.g. a tight oil drain plug) with the vehicle raised, unless it is properly supported and in a safe condition. Wherever possible, initially slacken tight fastenings before raising the car off the ground.

TAKE CARE to avoid touching any engine or exhaust system component unless it is cool enough so as not to burn you.

ALWAYS keep antifreeze, brake and clutch fluid away from vehicle paintwork. Wash off any spills immediately.

NEVER syphon fuel, antifreeze, brake fluid or other such toxic liquids by mouth, or allow prolonged contact with your skin. There is an increasing awareness that they can damage your health. Best of all, use a suitable hand pump and wear gloves.

ALWAYS work in a well ventilated area and don't inhale dust - it may contain asbestos or other poisonous substances.

WIPE UP any spilt oil, grease or water off the floor immediately, before there is an accident.

MAKE SURE that spanners and all other tools are the right size for the job and are not likely to slip. Never try to 'double-up' spanners to gain more leverage.

SEEK HELP if you need to lift something heavy which may be beyond your capability.

ALWAYS ensure that the safe working load rating of any jacks, hoists or lifting gear used is sufficient for the job, and is used only as recommended by the manufacturer.

NEVER take risky short-cuts or rush to finish a job. Plan ahead and allow plenty of time.

BE meticulous and keep the work area tidy - you'll avoid frustration, work better and loose less.

KEEP children and animals right away from the work area and from unattended vehicles.

ALWAYS wear eye protection when working under the vehicle or using any power tools.

BEFORE undertaking dirty jobs, use a barrier cream on your hands as a protection against infection. Preferably, wear thin gloves, available from DIY outlets.

DON'T lean over, or work on, a running engine unless strictly necessary, and keep long hair and loose clothing well out of the way of moving mechanical parts. Note that it is theoretically possible for fluorescent striplighting to make an engine fan appear to be stationary - check! This is the sort of error that happens when you're dog tired and not thinking straight. So don't work on your car when you're overtired!

REMOVE your wrist watch, rings and all other jewellery before doing any work on the vehicle - especially the electrical system.

ALWAYS tell someone what you're doing and have them regularly check that all is well, especially when working alone on, or under, the vehicle.

ALWAYS seek specialist advice if you're in doubt about any job. The safety of your vehicle affects you, your passengers and other road users.

FIRE

Petrol (gasoline) is a dangerous and highly flammable liquid requiring special precautions. When working on the fuel system, disconnect the vehicle battery earth (ground) terminal whenever possible and always work outside, or in a very well ventilated area. Any form of spark, such as that caused by an electrical fault, by two metal surfaces striking against each other, by a central heating boiler in the garage 'firing up', or even by static electricity built up in your clothing can, in a confined space, ignite petrol vapour causing an explosion. Take great care not to spill petrol on to the engine or exhaust system, never allow any naked flame anywhere near the work area and, above all, don't smoke.

1. Invest in a workshop-sized fire extinguisher. Choose the carbon dioxide type or preferably, dry powder but never a water type extinguisher for workshop use. Water conducts electricity and can make worse an oil or petrol-based fire, in certain circumstances.

FUMES

In addition to the fire dangers described previously, petrol (gasoline) vapour and the vapour from many solvents, thinners, and adhesives is highly toxic and under certain conditions can lead to unconsciousness or even death, if inhaled. The risks are increased if such fluids are used in a confined space so always ensure adequate ventilation when handling materials of this nature. Treat all such substances with care, always read the instructions and follow them implicitly.

Always ensure that the car is outside the work place in open air if the engine is running. Exhaust fumes contain poisonous carbon monoxide - even if the car is fitted with a catalytic converter, since 'cats' sometimes fail and don't function with the engine cold.

Never have the engine running with the car in the garage or in any enclosed space.

Inspection pits are another source of danger from the build-up of fumes. Never drain petrol (gasoline) or use solvents, thinners adhesives or other toxic substances in an inspection pit as the extremely confined space allows the highly toxic fumes to concentrate. Running the engine with the vehicle over the pit can have the same results. It is also dangerous to park a vehicle for any length of time over an inspection pit. The fumes from even a slight fuel leak can cause an explosion when the engine is started.

MAINS ELECTRICITY

Best of all, use rechargeable tools and a DC inspection lamp, powered from a remote 12V battery - both are much safer! However, if you do use a mains-powered inspection lamp, power tool etc, ensure that the appliance is wired correctly to its plug, that where necessary it is properly earthed (grounded), and that the fuse is of the correct rating for the appliance concerned. Do not use any mains powered equipment in damp conditions or in the vicinity of fuel, fuel vapour or the vehicle battery.

Also, before using any mains powered electrical equipment, take one more simple precaution - use an RCD (Residual Current Device) circuit breaker. Then, if there is a short, the RCD circuit breaker minimises the risk of electrocution by instantly cutting the power supply. Buy one from any electrical store or DIY centre. RCDs fit simply into your electrical socket before plugging in your electrical equipment.

SAFETY FIRST!

THE IGNITION SYSTEM

Extreme care must be taken when working on the ignition system with the ignition switched on or with the engine cranking or running.

Touching certain parts of the ignition system, such as the HT leads, distributor cap, ignition coil etc, can result in a severe electric shock. This is especially likely where the insulation on any of these components is weak, or if the components are dirty or damp. Note also that voltages produced by electronic ignition systems are much higher than conventional systems and could prove fatal, particularly to persons with cardiac pacemaker implants. Consult your handbook or main dealer if in any doubt. An additional risk of injury can arise while working on running engines, if the operator touches a high voltage lead and pulls his hand away on to a conductive or revolving part.

THE BATTERY

Don't smoke, or allow a naked light, or cause a spark near the vehicle's battery, even in a well ventilated area. A certain amount of highly explosive hydrogen gas will be given off as part of the normal charging process. Care should be taken to avoid sparking by switching off the power supply before charger leads are connected or disconnected. Battery terminals should be shielded, since a battery contains energy and a spark can be caused by any conductor which touches its terminals or exposed connecting straps.

Before working on the fuel or electrical systems, always disconnect the battery earth (ground) terminal.

When charging the battery from an external source, disconnect both battery leads before connecting the charger. If the battery is not of the 'sealed-for-life' type, loosen the filler plugs or remove the cover before charging. For best results the battery should be given a low rate 'trickle' charge overnight. Do not charge at an excessive rate or the battery may burst.

Always wear gloves and goggles when carrying or when topping up the battery. Even in diluted form (as it is in the battery) the acid electrolyte is extremely corrosive and must not be allowed to contact the eyes, skin or clothes.

BRAKES AND ASBESTOS

Whenever you work on the braking system mechanical components, or remove front or rear brake pads or shoes: i) wear an efficient particle mask, ii) wipe off all brake dust from the work area (never blow it off with compressed air), iii) dispose of brake dust and discarded shoes or pads in a sealed plastic bag, iv) wash hands thoroughly after you have finished working on the brakes and certainly before you eat or smoke, v) replace shoes and pads only with asbestos-free shoes or pads. Note that asbestos brake dust can cause cancer if inhaled.

Obviously, a car's brakes are among its most important safety related items. Do not dismantle your car's brakes unless you are fully competent to do so. If you have not been trained in this work, but wish to carry out the jobs described in this book, it is strongly recommend that you have a garage or qualified mechanic check your work before using the car on the road.

BRAKE FLUID

Brake fluid absorbs moisture rapidly from the air and can become dangerous resulting in brake failure. Catrol (UK) Ltd recommend that you should have your brake fluid tested at least once a year by a properly equipped garage with test equipment and you should change the fluid in accordance with your vehicle manufacturer's recommendations or as advised in this book if we recommend a shorter interval than the manufacturers. Always buy no more brake fluid than you need. Never store an open pack. Dispose of the remainder at your Local Authority Waste Disposal Site, in the designated disposal unit, *not* with general waste or with waste oil.

ENGINE OILS

Take care and observe the following precautions when working with used engine oil. Apart from the obvious risk of scalding when draining the oil from a hot engine, there is the danger from contaminates that are contained in all used oil.

Always wear disposable plastic or rubber gloves when draining the oil from your engine. i) Note that the drain plug and the oil are often hotter than you expect! Wear gloves if the plug is too hot to touch and keep your hand to one side so that you are not scalded by the spurt of oil as the plug comes away. ii) There are very real health hazards associated with used engine oil. In the words of one manufacturer's handbook, "Prolonged and repeated contact may cause serious skin disorders, including dermatitis and cancer". Use a barrier cream on your hands and try not to get oil on them. Where practicable, wear gloves and wash your hands with hand cleaner soon after carrying out the work. Keep oil out of the reach of children. iii) NEVER, EVER dispose of old engine oil into the ground or down a drain. In the UK, and in most EC countries, every local authority must provide a safe means of oil disposal. In the UK, try your local Environmental Health Department for advice on waste disposal facilities.

PLASTIC MATERIALS

Work with plastic materials brings additional hazards into workshops. Many of the materials used (polymers, resins, adhesives and materials acting as catalysts and accelerators) readily produce very dangerous situations in the form of poisonous fumes, skin irritants, risk of fire and explosions. Do not allow resin or 2-pack adhesive hardener, or that supplied with filler or 2-pack stopper to come into contact with skin or eyes. Read carefully the safety notes supplied on the can, tube or packaging.

JACK AND AXLE STANDS

Throughout this book you will see many references to the correct use of jacks, axle stands and similar equipment - and we make no apologies for being repetitive! This is one area where safety cannot be overstressed - your life could be at stake!

Special care must be taken when any type of lifting equipment is used. Jacks are made for lifting the vehicle only, not for supporting it. Never work under the car using only a jack to support the weight. Jacks must be supplemented by adequate additional means of support, such as axle stand, positioned under secure load-bearing parts of the frame or underbody. Drive-on ramps are limiting because of their design and size but they are simple to use, reliable and the most stable type of support, by far. We strongly recommend their use.

Full details on jacking and supporting the vehicle will be found in *Chapter 4, Raising the car.*

FLUOROELASTOMERS

MOST IMPORTANT! PLEASE READ THIS SECTION!

If you service your car in the normal way, none of the following may be relevant to you. Unless, for example, you encounter a car which has been on fire (even in a localised area), subject to heat in, say, a crash-damage repairer's shop or vehicle breaker's yard, or if any second-hand parts have been heated in any of these ways.

Many synthetic rubber-like materials used in motor cars contain a substance called fluorine. These materials are known as fluoroelastomers and are commonly used for oil seals, wiring and cabling, bearing surfaces, gaskets, diaphragms, hoses and 'O' rings. If they are subjected to temperatures greater than 315 degrees C, they will decompose and can be potentially hazardous. Fluoroelastomer materials will show physical signs of decomposition under such conditions in the form of charring of black sticky masses. Some decomposition may occur at temperatures above 200 degrees C, and it is obvious that when a car has been in a fire or has been dismantled with the assistance of a cutting torch or blow torch, the fluoroelastomers can decompose in the manner indicated above.

In the presence of any water or humidity, including atmospheric moisture, the by-products caused by the fluoroelastomers being heated can be extremely dangerous. According to the Health and Safety Executive, "Skin contact with this liquid or decomposition residues can cause painful and penetrating burns. Permanent irreversible skin and tissue damage can occur". Damage can also be caused to eyes or by the inhalation of fumes created as fluoroelastomers are burned or heated.

After fires or exposure to high temperatures observe the following precautions:

1. *Do not touch blackened or charred seals or equipment.*

2. *Allow all burnt or decomposed fluoroelastomer materials to cool down before inspection, investigations, tear-down or removal.*

3. *Preferably, don't handle parts containing decomposed fluoroelastomers, but if you must, wear goggles and PVC (polyvinyl chloride) or neoprene protective gloves whilst doing so. Never handle such parts unless they are completely cool.*

4. *Contaminated parts, residues, materials and clothing, including protective clothing and gloves, should be disposed of by an approved contractor to landfill or by incineration according to national or local regulations. Oil seals, gaskets and 'O' rings, along with contaminated material, must not be burned locally.*

WORKSHOP SAFETY - GENERAL

1. *Always have a fire extinguisher of the correct type at arm's length when working on the fuel system - under the car, or under the bonnet.*

   If you do have a fire, DON'T PANIC. Use the extinguisher effectively by directing it at the base of the fire.

2. *NEVER use a naked flame near petrol or anywhere in the workplace.*

3. *KEEP your inspection lamp well away from any source of petrol (gasoline) such as when disconnecting a carburettor float bowl or fuel line.*

4. *NEVER use petrol (gasoline) to clean parts. Use paraffin (kerosene) or white spirits.*

5. *NO SMOKING! There's a risk of fire or transferring dangerous substances to your mouth and, in any case, ash falling into mechanical components is to be avoided!*

6. *BE METHODICAL in everything you do, use common sense, and think of safety at all times.*

CHAPTER 2 - BUYING SPARES

Another advantage of DIY servicing is that you can choose what parts you buy, where you buy your parts, and how much you pay for them, whereas if the dealer services your car you buy his parts at his price - which is likely to be rather more (sometimes considerably more!) than you would need to pay elsewhere.

Of course, the dealer will claim that the cheaper parts, bought elsewhere, are 'spurious', whereas his are 'genuine' - which is strange, because quite often the 'spurious' part will prove to be precisely the same item but maybe only half the price of the 'genuine' article!

This is because many of the car makers' parts are actually made by independent manufacturers - so, to take, for instance, a far from spurious brand, a part made by Bosch would be sold as a Bosch part, in Bosch packaging, in an independent car parts store, but might appear as a VW part, in a VW box, or as a Vauxhall part, in a Vauxhall box, in the car dealer parts departments.

It doesn't mean to say that there aren't genuinely spurious parts around, or that the independent store's part will always be half-price. Or that some of the franchised car dealer parts departments won't surprise you with an even lower price than at a cut-price independent!

1. There are three main numbers you will need to know in order to buy parts and touch-up paint for your car. The VIN (Vehicle Identification Number) is your car's internationally unique number and tells your parts supplier *exactly* which model and year the car is. (On older vehicles, you will find the maker's own 'chassis number'.) Quote the VIN whenever you buy spares for your car. The VIN plate position will be shown in your handbook and the number should be the same as that shown on your vehicle documents ('V5' document in the UK; 'Title' document in the USA).

2. The engine number may also be shown on the VIN plate; it should certainly be on the engine! Once again, check your handbook for its location and - as with the VIN number - enter onto *page 1, Auto-Biography* of this book.

INSIDE INFORMATION: If you need an exact paint colour match, you'll need the car's paint code number. See the VIN plate (again!), or a paint code plate inside the fuel filler cap, the tailgate or some other place - see your handbook, again.

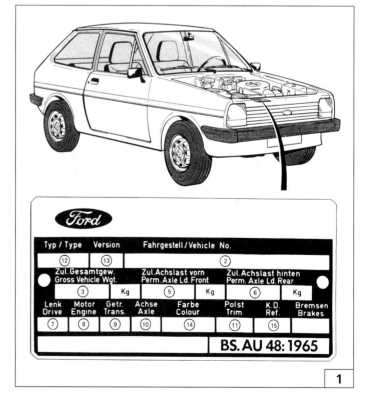

SOURCES

MAIN DEALERS

How can you identify 'quality'? It's sometimes difficult, but parts from your car's main dealer are certain to be so and, of course, they will be 'genuine' items with a comprehensive warranty (sometimes this is much longer than normal). In addition, the parts counter staff will be familiar with the vehicles, and should be only too pleased to help owners locate the spares required. If required, they can usually locate an elusive part at another dealership. Prices are occasionally reduced from the usual retail level - watch for special offers which are often listed at the parts counter.

When buying spares, have your car's 'personal' details to hand - the date of registration and its chassis (or VIN) and engine numbers. These can be helpful where parts changed during production, and can be the key to a more helpful approach by some parts salespeople! You may, by now have entered this key information on the Auto-Biography pages at the front of this book, for ease of reference. Your handbook will show you where to find the relevant information on your car.

PARTS FACTORS/MOTOR ACCESSORY SHOPS

Local parts factors and motor accessory shops can be extremely useful for obtaining servicing parts at short notice - many 'accessory' outlets open late in the evening, and on both days at weekends. However, as they tend to concentrate on more 'mainstream' models, if you own an older, classic car or slightly 'offbeat' car, you will have to be very specific about your requirements to avoid ending up with a part that is 'almost right' rather than just what you want.

Don't overlook the 'trade' motor factors outlets in the UK. One of the biggest (and a supplier of some of the parts used in this series of books) is Partco, with branches all over the country - find them in Yellow Pages.

BUYING AT THE COUNTER

If you're buying spares 'in person' rather than by post, try to avoid Saturday and Sunday mornings - weekends are often very busy for parts counters, and you may find the staff have more time to help you if you visit early on a weekday morning, or in the evening, while on your way to or from work. At these times you are also less likely to have to queue for a long time! On the other hand, main dealers are often at their busiest first thing in the day, when other motor traders often turn up for their spares.

3

3. ORDERING SPARES BY POST

Most specialists offer a postal service, with payment being by credit card. The points to check are a) the cost of carriage, b) whether VAT is included and b) if there is a cut-off point where you don't pay carriage, or where it is cheaper. For example, it could be that orders over £20 are not subject to a £5 carriage charge. If your order comes to £18, you'd be better off adding a set of points or plugs or something of that nature to it, rather than pay £5 for 'nothing'. Common to most specialists is a policy of offering a choice of quality on many items. These will usually carry a note to the effect that they are O/E (original equipment) quality, or otherwise and usually the country of origin. It's true to say that some 'pattern' parts are just about as good as the originals; it's equally true to say that some certainly aren't! Some of the body panels, for example, leave something to be desired in terms of fit and finish. Which you choose will depend on the depth of your wallet and whether or not you want to stay 'original'. However, we would always recommend buying the best quality braking, steering and suspension products you can, regardless of price, because your life depends on them.

BUYING SECONDHAND

If you run a classic car, you could consider buying spares from an 'autojumble'. Overall, these tend to comprise private owners selling off used or unwanted stock and dealers clearing out their parts shelves. Naturally, you need consider very seriously what it is you're buying. Purchasing any safety items - braking, steering, suspension - without being absolutely sure of their provenance is dangerous indeed, and not something we would recommend. Even if you're helping a dealer unload some surplus stock, the odds are it has been standing for some years. Make sure that safety-related parts are still serviceable and are not, for example, covered in a fine coating of rust.

That's not to decry buying secondhand altogether. Buying, say, a distributor, or carburettor which you know to be 'low mileage' units, to replace your worn out components makes great sense. Equally, trim panels and other interior parts can often be obtained at a fraction of the new cost.

BUYING SPARES

CHECKS ON RUNNING GEAR COMPONENTS

Always take very great care when purchasing 'hardware' for the steering, suspension and braking systems, which are obviously vital for safety.

Although many outlets sell 'reconditioned' components on an 'exchange' basis, the quality of workmanship and the extent of the work carried out on such units can vary greatly. Therefore, if buying a rebuilt unit, always check particularly carefully when buying. It has to be said that, wherever possible, reconditioned units are best obtained from main dealers, or from reputable specialist suppliers. Always talk to fellow owners before buying - they may be able to direct you to a supplier offering sound parts at reasonable prices. When buying, always enquire about the terms of the guarantee (if any!).

In any event, the following notes should help you make basic checks on some of the commonly required components:

BRAKES

(Purchase NEW parts ONLY): Look for boxes bearing genuine main dealer or well-known brake manufacturer.

STEERING

Ball joints, king pins, steering boxes, rack and pinion steering units, etc, - buy new, again rejecting any moisture-damaged stock.

Steering racks (and boxes) are invariably available as exchange items. Ensure that you rotate the operating shaft fully from lock to lock, feeling for any undue free play, roughness, stiffness, or 'notchiness' as you do so. Reject any units showing signs of any of these problems.

SUSPENSION

Used shock absorbers really aren't worth buying on a used basis - standard units for most models are available incredibly cheaply from specialist suppliers. Don't forget that shock absorbers should always be replaced in pairs and preferably in complete sets of four.

HOWEVER, we would strongly advise against buying secondhand brake, suspension, and steering components, unless you know the source of the parts, and really are sure that they are in first class condition. Even then, be sure that you see the vehicle they have been taken from, and avoid any such parts from accident-damaged cars.

In every case, ensure that the components you are buying are compatible with your particular vehicle, and carry out basic checks to ensure that they too are not badly worn.

TYRES

For the ultimate in long life, roadholding and wet grip, brand new radial tyres from a reputable manufacturer offer the best solution, especially where the car is used all year round, on an 'everyday' basis. Remould tyres are available at lower initial cost, but life expectancy is not as long as with new tyres and we don't recommend them. Secondhand tyre outlets are becoming increasingly common lately, most selling used tyres imported from the continent, where tyre laws are more stringent than in the U.K. However, if you purchase such tyres, you are taking a risk in that you have no knowledge of the history of the tyres or what has happened to them, how they have been repaired, and so on. A report conducted by the RAC revealed that a very high percentage of tyres in their test sample had very dangerous faults, such as damaged walling. Their advice, and we would agree, is to stick to top quality, unused tyres from a reputable manufacturer. They may cost a little more, but at least you will have peace of mind, and should be able to rely on their performance in all road and weather situations. After all, your life - and those of other road users - could depend on it!

CONCLUSION

Finally, if you want to buy quality and save money, you must be prepared to shop around. Ring each of your chosen suppliers with a shopping list to hand and your car's personal data, from the Auto-Biography at the front of this book, in front of you. Keep a written note of prices - including VAT, delivery etc - whether the parts are proper 'brand name' parts or not and - most importantly! - whether or not the parts you want are in stock. Parts expected 'soon' have been known never to materialise. A swivel pin in the hand is worth two in the bush! (Bad pun!)

CHAPTER 3 - TOOLS & EQUIPMENT

Although good tools are not cheap, if you reckon their cost against what you would otherwise spend on professional servicing and repairs, your arithmetic should show you that it doesn't take long to recoup your outlay - and then to start showing a profit!

In fact, there is no need to spend a fortune all at once - most owners who do their own servicing acquire their implements over a long period of time. However, there are some items you simply cannot do without in order properly to carry out the work necessary to keep your car on the road. Therefore, in the following lists, we have concentrated on those items which are likely to be valuable aids to maintaining your car in a good state of tune, and to keep it running sweetly and safely and in addition we have featured some of the tools that are 'nice-to-have' rather than 'must have' because as your tool chest grows, there are some tools that help to make servicing just that bit easier and more thorough to carry out.

Two vital points - firstly always buy the best quality tools you can afford. 'Cheap and cheerful' items may look similar to more expensive implements, but experience shows that they often fail when the going gets tough, and some can even be dangerous. With proper care, good quality tools will last a lifetime, and can be regarded as an investment. The extra outlay is well worth it, in the long run.

A fairly basic kit will tackle most servicing needs, plus some items of workshop equipment, plus some handy 'tuning' aids that have become available to the DIY market over recent years at affordable prices.

There are further items which can undoubtedly make life easier, and save money - but they could be a wee bit costly in the first place. Perhaps the answer is to share their benefits (and so their cost!) with like-minded DIY friends.

Over the years, there have been various nut/bolt/spanner designations. For many years British cars standardised on 'AF', a designation referring to the measurement 'across the flats' of the hexagon nut or bolt head, while the 'Foreigners' were 'Metric'. While there are still many 'AF' cars around, all modern cars are 'Metric' of course, apart from American cars. For the record, 'metric' sizes are also measured across their flats!). Be sure you know what designation applies to your car before you start buying. Your local motor accessory store should be able to advise - and if they can't shop elsewhere. Call your local main dealer to make sure, if necessary.

SPANNERS:

A. The two common types of spanner are the ring and the open-ended. The ring spanner grips practically all round the bolt, and is preferable where the bolt is really tight, for an open-ended spanner, merely straddling two flats of the bolt, could slip. On the other hand, the open-end is often quicker and easier to use - so this set of 'Combination' spanners, a ring at one end, open-ended the other, is a nice compromise!

A

Our thanks are due, for their kind assistance with this chapter, to Sykes-Pickavant Ltd, who supplied most of the hand tools shown here and in use in the servicing sections, similarly to Polcar-Belco Ltd, who supplied the 'Lock and Lift' trolley jack, and to Gunson Ltd, who supplied the tuning aids, again seen both here and in the servicing text.

B. While the straight 'flatness' of the combinations (or of a conventional open-ended spanner) is often useful, there are occasions when only the offset, or 'swan neck' of the conventional ring spanner will do the job - like when having to operate over the top of one bolt in order to undo another.

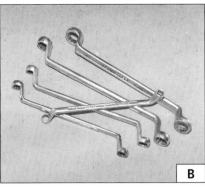

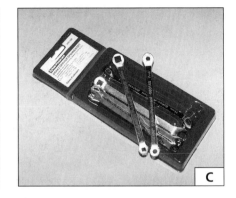

Unlike the combinations, the conventional ring and open-ended spanners will have a different size at each end. Usually, the AF sizes will rise in sixteenths of an inch, and the metrics by one millimetre - the following sizes will probably cover most of your needs:
AF - 3/8 x 7/16, 1/2 x 9/16, 5/8 x 11/16, 13/16 x 7/8
Metric - 10 x 11, 12 x 13, 14 x 15, 16 x 17

C. The sturdy specialist brake spanner, for brake adjusters or bleed nipples, is undeniably a wise buy, as mentioned in the brake servicing text. You might not need the set as shown here, but you can choose individual sizes to suit your car, such as 1/4 in. sq x 11/32 in. sq, or 1/4 in. hex x 5/16 in. AF, or perhaps 8 x 10mm hex - there are others.

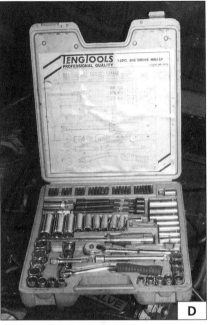

D. It was once thought of as a luxury, but nowadays at least a basic socket set should figure highly on your shopping list, for it will cover your basic spanner sizes and can often solve difficult access or extra-leverage problems. This one is a fairly sophisticated Teng Tools set, and includes a number of useful extras, such as spark plug spanners and Allen key and screwdriver bits.

E. A torque wrench was also once a luxury, but nowadays it's practically essential, with specific torque settings quoted for many of the nuts and bolts used in modern car engineering. The example shown will cater for most applications, including adjustable wheel-bearing hub nuts, but even the next size up (30-150 lb/ft) in the DIY range will still fall short of the 200-odd lb/ft specified for some hub nuts!

F. If you still need a plug spanner, and particularly if your engine features deep-set spark plugs, this Sykes-Pickavant 'extra long plug wrench', combining both 10mm and 14mm sizes, could be a boon. Some plugs are set deeper than the average length of a socket-set spark plug spanner, and if the socket set's extension bar is prone to leaving the spanner socket stuck on the plug, then you could have a problem ...

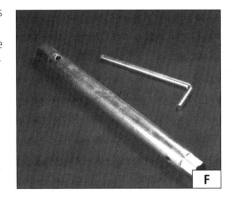

SCREWDRIVERS:

G. You will need a selection of screwdrivers, both flat-bladed and cross-headed, long ones, short ones, slim ones, fat ones ...

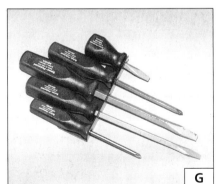

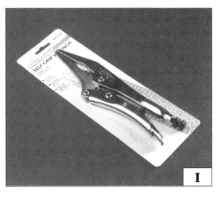

PLIERS:

H. Ordinary combination (or 'engineers') pliers are needed for general work, while a long-nosed pair are handy where access is tight. Their cutting edges are useful for stripping cable insulation, or for snipping wire or trimming split-pin lengths, but you might prefer a pair of specialist side-cutter pliers for such work.

I. Jolly useful as an extra pair of hands, or for gripping such as a rusty nut or bolt really tightly, is a self-grip wrench. This is a long-nose example, but there are also ordinary straight-jaw and round jaw versions.

SUNDRIES:

J. You'll need hammers, including the useful 1lb ball-pein type, plus a hefty copper hammer and maybe a soft (plastic-headed) hammer, too.

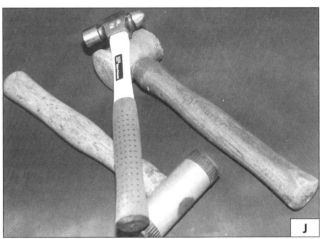

K. The wire brush should have brass bristles and as well as an ordinary set of feeler gauges, an 'ignition set' covers most plug and points gap sizes, and includes a points file and a gap setting tool.

L. You may need a grease gun, you will want an oil can, and an oil funnel, and a container of sufficient capacity in to which the engine oil can be drained.

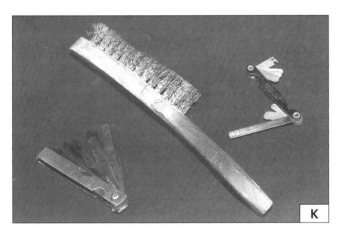

M. You may also need a drain plug 'key' suitable for your car unless all the drain plugs are 'bolt'-type hexagons.

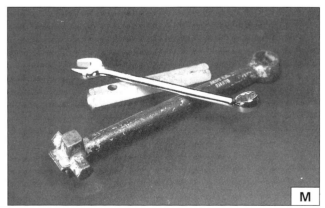

N. Well worthwhile, since some oil filters can be cussedly tight, is some sort of oil filter wrench - the chain-type by Sykes-Pickavant is a nice example. See Job 45 for how it's used.

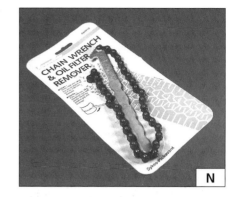

N

O. A separate set of hand-held Allen keys is a good idea (they come in metric or Imperial sizes), and an adjustable spanner and a 'Junior' hacksaw will have their uses.

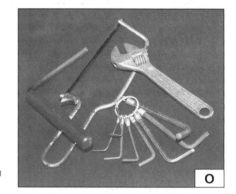

O

P. For your weekly maintenance checks, you'll need a tyre pressure gauge, tyre tread depth gauge and a footpump - which might, like the example here, have an integral pressure gauge. And whether you're wheel-changing at home or roadside, you will welcome the extremely useful Sykes-Pickavant 'Wheelmaster' wrench, which can be extended to give enough leverage to shift those wheel nuts or bolts that the average car-kit wheelbrace wouldn't even look at - see 'Wheel-Change Routine' elsewhere in this book. Remember to carry it with you in the car!

LIFTING:

Q. While the jack supplied with the car might be OK for emergency wheel-changes, you would soon tire of trying to use it for servicing operations. Here you need a good trolley jack, and one of the latest on the market is this 2-ton lifting capacity Belcar 'Lift and Lock' example which, as its name suggests, has a built-in fail-safe locking device in the event of hydraulic failure.

P

R. However, although their unique safety feature offers extra peace of mind, Belcar still warn that you should not venture beneath a car supported on a jack alone. Having raised it, you need to support it safely and securely. What you need now is definitely NOT house bricks (or any other such potentially dangerous items!) but rather axle stands or wheel-ramps. The adjustable-height stands are Paddy Hopkirk brand, the ramps are of both unknown vintage or make! If you don't need the wheels off, it can be argued that the ramps offer better stability - though you'll not always have the room (or the nerve!) to actually drive up onto them.

TUNING AIDS:

S. As we have said earlier in this chapter and within the servicing sections, the tuning aids that are now available to the DIY market have become practically invaluable 'musts' for the dedicated home mechanic. Any of the Gunson's collection shown here would soon prove their worth. Top of the tree, of course, is their 'Gastester Professional' - don't let its designation suggest that it's not for DIY use, for although it's expensive a group of friends sharing its cost would find their outlay well worth the benefits offered by the unit's Exhaust Gas 'CO' functions, plus its Voltage, Dwell and RPM modes. If it's pure 'multi-meter' you're after, then their 'Digimeter 320' is a tidy little hand-held unit, with clear digital read-outs for such as Volts (DC and household AC) and Amps, Ohms, RPM, and Dwell (degrees and per cent), and its sophistication extends to Frequency, Period and Pulsewidth testing (handy for fuel injection systems), as well as Diode, Resistance and Continuity testing. Also by Gunson's is the powerful 'Timestrobe' xenon timing light, the now not so new, but still novel 'Colortune' and (not shown) the 'Carbalancer', the latter two devices are also mentioned in the carburettor tuning text.

Q

R

S

CHAPTER 4 - RAISING THE CAR

Part I - Raising The Car In The Workshop

RAISING A CAR - SAFELY!
You will often need to raise your car off the ground in order to carry out the Service Jobs shown here. To start off with, here's what you must never do - never work beneath a car held on a jack, not even a trolley jack. Quite a number of deaths have been caused by a car slipping off a jack while someone has been working beneath. On the other hand, the safest way is by raising a car on a proprietary brand of ramps. Sometimes, there is no alternative but to use axle stands. Please read all of the following information and act upon it!

I

II

III

When using car ramps:

(I) Make absolutely certain that the ramps are parallel to the wheels of the car and that the wheels are exactly central on each ramp.

Always have an assistant watch both sides of the car as you drive up. Drive up to the end 'stops' on the ramps but never over them!

INSIDE INFORMATION: wrap a strip of carpet into a loop around the first 'rung' of the ramps and drive over the doubled-up piece of carpet on the approach to the ramps. This prevents the ramps from skidding away, as they are inclined to do, as the car is driven on to them.

Apply the hand brake firmly, put the car in first or reverse gear, or 'Park', in the case of an automatic.

(II) Chock both wheels remaining on the ground, both in front and behind so that the car can't move in either direction.

On other occasions, you might need to work on the car while it is supported on an axle stand or a pair of axle stands. These are inherently less stable than ramps and so you must take much greater care when working beneath them. In particular:

• ensure that the axle stand is on flat, stable ground, never on a surface where one side can sink in to the ground.

• ensure that the car is on level ground and that the hand brake is off and the transmission in neutral.

• raise the car with a trolley jack - invest in one if you don't already own one; the car's wheel changing jack is often too unstable. Place a piece of cloth over the head of the jack if your car is nicely finished on the underside. Ensure that the floor is sufficiently clear and smooth for the trolley jack wheels to roll as the car is raised and lowered, otherwise it could slip off the jack.

(III) Place the jack beneath the front subframe or another load-bearing area, with a block of wood to spread the load when raising the front of the car...

(IV) ...and place the axle stands beneath body-mounts or suspension mounts, but NEVER under the engine or gearbox.

(V) At the rear of the car, place the jack head, with a block of wood to spread the load, beneath the rear body jacking points or rear suspension mounting points.

(VI) Take care to locate the top of the axle stands on a strong, level, stable part of the car's underside: you should never use a movable suspension part (because the part can move and allow the axle stand to slip) or the floor of the car (which is just too weak).

Just as when using ramps - only even more importantly! - apply the hand brake firmly, put the car in first or reverse gear (or 'Park', in the case of an automatic) and chock both wheels remaining on the ground, both in front and behind.

Be especially careful when applying force to a spanner or when pulling hard on anything, when the car is supported off the ground. It is all too easy to move the car so far that it topples off the axle stands. And remember that if a car falls on you, **YOU COULD BE KILLED!**

Whenever working beneath a car, have someone primed to keep an eye on you! If someone pops out to see how you are getting on every quarter of an hour or so, it could be enough to save your life!

Do remember that, in general, a car will be more stable when only one wheel is removed and one axle stand used than if two wheels are removed in conjunction with two axle stands. You are strongly advised never to work on the car with all four wheels off the ground, on four axle stands. The car would then be very unstable and dangerous to work beneath.

Before lowering the car to the ground, remember to remove the chocks, release the hand brake and place the transmission in neutral.

Part II - Raising The Car In An Emergency

SAFETY FIRST!
Wheel changing jacks are dreadfully unstable! Take great care not to get any part of your body under the car when supported by one of these jacks.

It happens too often - a roadside puncture, probably in the dark, probably in the rain, the spare is flat, you don't know where the car jack is, or the wheelbrace, and even if you did you don't know where the jack should go, and the wheel nuts are far too tight to be shifted by that bit of bent rod they call a wheelbrace! If you've never done it before, changing a wheel is a daunting prospect, so practise the wheel-change routine at home, before the worst happens to you.

RAISING THE CAR

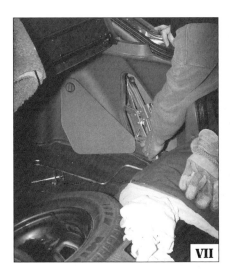

(VII) START by finding where the jack and the wheelbrace are normally stowed. CHECK that the spare hasn't gone flat, because you check it every week, along with the other wheels/tyres. PREPARE by ensuring that in the boot and/or glovebox you have an old waterproof, something to kneel on, a rag to clean your hands if necessary, but also protective gloves, and a torch.

(VIII) Wheel nuts should be done up to a specified degree of tightness, but all too often they're done up by a chap behaving like a gorilla with a toothache! Give yourself a better chance by buying one of these extendible wrenches, complete with the right-sized socket to fit your wheel nuts or bolts. Its superior strength and leverage will shift wheel nuts that the car-kit brace wouldn't even look at - it's an absolute 'must', not just for those who haven't got the strength of a raging gorilla but to replace that feeble wheel brace in the boot, for everyone!

(IX) In many instances, you will first have to lever off a wheeltrim - or plastic caps over the nuts that look like the real thing but are not! The car-kit wheelbrace might have a flattened end made for the job, otherwise find yourself perhaps a suitable screwdriver (keep it in the car) and lever carefully around the circumference of the trim: note where the tyre valve protrudes through, making a pencil mark if necessary. Once the wheeltrim is partly unclipped - it often needs vigorous levering, so watch that bodywork! - you may be better off doning your gloves and pulling.

(X) With the wheel still on the ground, loosen the wheel nuts. For your physical wellbeing you should always bear down on the wheelbrace, rather than pull it upwards - if you're stuck with that bent-rod car-kit brace, you'll probably need a length of pipe to slip over it to extend its leverage but it will probably be a struggle to keep it on the nut... If you try slackening the wheel nuts *after* you've raised the wheel, all you'll do is rotate the wheel, not the nut!

RAISING THE CAR

(XI) Make sure now that you know exactly where and how the car jack locates, and how it is operated: some might have a projection that plugs into a hole in the sill (you would first remove a rubber plug from the hole) others might straddle a particular stretch beneath the sill, some might lift both wheels clear of the ground from just one location, others might have a choice of two locations for front or rear wheel - if you are unsure, or if your handbook doesn't make it clear, seek the advice of your car dealer. Do it NOW, so that you'll know when you need it!

Also carry a piece of timber in the boot that can be placed beneath the jack to spread the load and prevent it from sinking into soft ground. Have the handbrake on, and there are purpose-made chocks you can wedge each side of the wheel opposite to the one you are changing to guard against the car rolling. Wind the jack handle until the required wheel is clear of the ground, remembering if it's flat that you need enough clearance for a wheel with a fully pumped up tyre - do not put any part of your body beneath a car which is supported only on a jack.

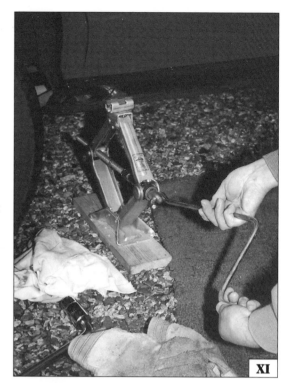

(XII) SAFETY FIRST! and INSIDE INFORMATION
Always place the spare wheel, or the wheel you've just removed, under the car: partly for safety to help guard against being crushed; partly so that if the car topples off the wheel-change jack (and they CAN, especially on soft ground) you'll be able to reposition the jack and start again.

(XIII) Once the required wheel is clear of the ground, fully undo the nuts or bolts, leaving one 'at the top' until last so you can get your balance and a secure grip before lifting away the wheel. Fitting the replacement wheel is easier where studs and nuts are used, because the studs give the wheel a positive location: but where bolts are used, it can be a bit of a struggle to try to locate the wheel on something (maybe some sort of projection on the hub/drum face) while you attempt to align the bolt holes and insert at least one bolt with one hand while steadying the wheel with the other! Nip the nuts/bolts up finger-tight, then lower the wheel to the ground for final tightening, working diagonally, a little at a time, on each nut/bolt: do them up as tight as you can, using all your strength if it's the car-kit wheelbrace, slightly less than full strength if it's the extended wrench. (Note that if the nuts are 'domed', the domed end fits against the wheel).

INSIDE INFORMATION: i) If your car's wheels are held on with bolts, have your local garage supply you with two pieces of threaded rod: bolts with heads cut off would be ideal. You can screw them into two of the holes in the hub, 'hang' the wheel on them while you put in the 'proper' wheel bolts to the other holes, then unscrew them with your fingers and fit the two remaining wheel retaining bolts. Remember to carry them with you! ii) You can also try levering the wheel up into place with a shovel, a length of wood or anything else you can lay your hands on, by the roadside.

Please read the whole of the Introduction to this Chapter before carrying out any work on your car.

SERVICE INTERVALS, STEP-BY-STEP

CHAPTER 5 - SERVICE SCHEDULES

Everyone wants to own a car that starts first time, runs reliably and lasts longer than the average. And there's no magic about how to put your car into that category, it's all a question of thorough maintenance! If you follow the Service Jobs listed here or have a garage or mechanic do it for you - you can almost *guarantee* that your car will still be going strong when others have fallen by the wayside... or the hard shoulder.

And if you don't know where to start, that's where this book comes in! If you want your car to be as well looked after as possible, you'll follow the Jobs shown here, but if you don't want to go all the way, you can pick and choose from the most essential items in the list. But do bear in mind that the Jobs we recommend are there for some very good reasons:

◆ *body maintenance* is rarely included in most service schedules. We believe it to be essential.

◆ *preventative maintenance* figures very high on our list of priorities. And that's why so many of our service jobs have the word "Check..." near the start!

◆ *older vehicles* need more jobs doing on them than new cars - it's as simple as that - so we list the jobs you will need to carry out in order to keep any car in fine fettle.

Using the Service Schedules

At the start of each Service Job, you'll see a heading in bold type, looking a bit like this:

☐ **Job 46. Spark plugs.**

Following the heading will be all the information you will need to enable you to carry out that particular Job. Please note that different models of car might have different settings. Please check your handbook for details.

Also, note that exactly the same Job numbers and headings will be found in the Service History chapter, where you will want to keep a full record of all the work you have carried out. After you have finished servicing your car, you will be able to tick off all of the jobs that you have completed and so, service by service, build up a complete Service History of work carried out on your car.

You will also find other key information immediately after each Job title and in most cases, there will be reference to an illustration - a photograph or line drawing, whichever is easier for you to follow - usually on the same page.

Other special headings are also used. One reads **INSIDE INFORMATION**. This tells you that here is a Job or a special tip that you wouldn't normally get to hear about, other than through the experience and 'inside' knowledge of the experts. Another is **SPECIALIST SERVICE**, which means that we recommend you to have this work carried out by a specialist. Some jobs, such as setting the tracking or suspension are best done with the right measuring equipment while other jobs may demand the use of equipment such as an exhaust gas analyser. Where we think you are better off having the work done for you, we say so!

Our thanks are due to the following companies for their kind permission to use line drawings. In each case, copyright is retained by the company in question. Ford Customer Service Division - Europe, Gunson Ltd and V.A.G. (United Kingdom) Ltd.

SAFETY FIRST!
*The other special heading is the one that could be the most important one of all! SAFETY FIRST! information must always be read with care and always taken seriously. In addition, please read the whole of **Chapter 1, Safety First!** before carrying out any work on your car. There are many hazards associated with working on a car but all of them can be avoided by adhering strictly to the safety rules. Don't skimp on safety!*

The 'Catch-up' Service

When you first buy a used car, you never know for sure just how well it's been looked after. Even one with a full service history is unlikely to have been serviced as thoroughly as one with a Porter Publishing Service Guide history! So, if you want to catch-up on all the servicing that may have been neglected on your car, just work through the entire list of Service Jobs listed for the *36,000 miles - or every thirty six months service*, add on the 'Longer Term servicing' Jobs, and your car will be bang up to date and serviced as well as you could hope for. Do allow several days for all of this work, not least because it will almost certainly throw up a number of extra jobs - potential faults that have been lurking beneath the surface - all of which will need putting right before you can 'sign off' your car as being in tip-top condition.

The Service History

Those people fortunate enough to own a new car, or one that has been well maintained from new will have the opportunity to keep a service record, or 'Service History' of their car, usually filled in by a main dealer. Until now, it hasn't been possible for the owner of an older car to keep a formal record of servicing but now you can, using the complete tick list in *Appendix 4* at the back of this book. In fact, you can go one better than the owners of those new cars, because your car's *Service History* will be more complete and more detailed than any manufacturer's service record, with the extra bonus that there is space for you to keep a record of all of those extra items that crop up from time to time. New tyres; replacement exhaust; extra accessories; where can you show those on a regular service schedule? Now you can, so if your battery goes down only 11 months after buying it, you'll be able to look up where and when you bought it. All you'll have to do is remember to fill in your Service Schedule in the first place!

500 Miles, Weekly, or Before Long Journeys, Whichever Comes First

☐ **Job 1. Engine oil level.**

Although some engines barely need their sump oil topping-up between major services, even healthy ones sometimes have an unusual appetite for it, while worn ones will certainly burn it. New or old can develop an oil leak. An engine low on oil runs the risk of internal damage, over-heating and eventual seizure - all of them ruining the engine.

Before you check the oil level, the engine should be switched off and left standing for a while to ensure that all oil has returned to the sump - obviously first thing in the morning after garaging overnight is the ideal time.

1A. Obviously, too, the car should be on level ground when you check the dipstick. Your handbook should identify the stick's location, but if not look for a 'ring pull' disappearing into a tube or hole on the side of the engine. Withdraw the stick and wipe it dry on lint-free clean cloth. There will usually be 'maximum' and 'minimum' marks on the stick and some handbooks will quote a specific quantity of oil for the difference between the two.

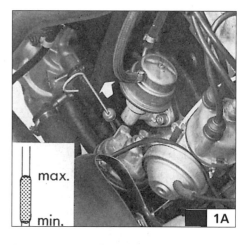

1B. Reinsert the dipstick then withdraw it again - the oil level will be seen on the dipstick and should be on or pretty close to the maximum (or 'max') mark, not close to the minimum (or 'min') mark. The lower mark is, of course, the danger level. But it could also be unwise to exceed the maximum mark - a shade over won't matter, but substantial over-filling can also lead to over-heating and other problems.

INSIDE INFORMATION: If your car's dipstick has to snake along a curved tube, and especially if the oil is fresh and clear, you might have difficulty in seeing the oil level. Dip, wipe and re-dip several times, turning the stick so that it goes into the tube from different angles, if possible - sometimes oil is wiped on or off the dipstick as it is withdrawn and

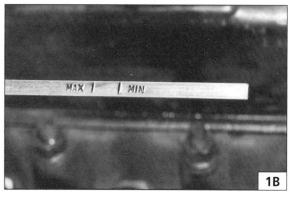

replaced, but only on one side. If it's the side with the markings on, put the stick in the other way round.

1C. If you do need to top up, do so a little at a time, through the oil filler normally found on the valve cover at the top of the engine. Allow time for the new oil to reach the sump before you re-check the level, not forgetting to start with a clean dipstick again.

1C

1D. Most oil filler caps unscrew 1/4 turn and lift off.

1E. A few screw all the way in and out. Don't force them down too tight when refitting.

1D

☐ **Job 2. Coolant level.**

> **SAFETY FIRST!**
> **i) The coolant level should be checked WHEN THE SYSTEM IS COLD. If you remove the pressure cap when the engine is hot, the release of pressure can cause the water in the cooling system to boil and spurt several feet in the air with the risk of severe scalding. ii) Take precautions to prevent anti-freeze coming in contact with the skin or eyes. If this should happen, rinse immediately with plenty of water.**

Again, this is a check that should be made first thing in the morning, before the engine has been run. There are two reasons for this: (i) Hot coolant expands, so you'll only get a true level reading when it's cold; (ii) Hot coolant (like a boiling kettle) can be extremely dangerous, and removal of the filler cap can release a scalding blast of steam and liquid. See *Safety First!* above,

2A. NEVER ATTEMPT TO REMOVE THE FILLER CAP WHEN THE ENGINE IS HOT. If, in an emergency, the cap needs to be removed before the engine has completely cooled,

wrap a rag around both the cap and your hands and open the cap in two stages, the first quarter turn to release any remaining internal pressure.

Generally speaking, an engine is at its most efficient when running at a temperature close to that of boiling water - and generally speaking it is water, with an anti-freeze content, that is used for the coolant. And water under pressure can reach a higher temperature than normal without boiling, thus avoiding all the attendant dangers of its dissipating away in steam, or even 'exploding' the system!

1E

2A

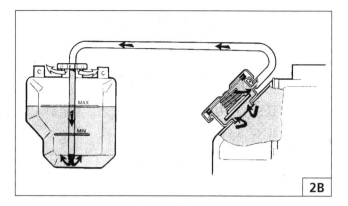

2B. The integral valve mechanism of a pressure cap will allow pressure within the system to build to a pre-determined level, say, 7 or 13 psi. At whichever point, a valve in the cap is forced open, allowing further pressure to vent to atmosphere (older system) or (modern system, as shown here) letting the expanding coolant out of the main radiator and into the expansion tank. As the engine cools, so does the coolant, which then begins to contract, causing a vacuum to start building within the system. This sucks open another valve in the cap, the suction then drawing (respectively) either air back in or, with modern systems, the previously expelled coolant back from the expansion tank.

2C. When cold, the coolant level in an old system should be just below the radiator filler neck...

2D ...or up to the level mark scribed on the expansion tank of a modern system. Where necessary, top up with clean water mixed with the percentage of anti-freeze (e.g., 25%, 33% or 50%) as recommended in your handbook - see reference to anti-freeze at the *12,000-mile/12-month service*.

☐ Job 3. Brake fluid level.

SAFETY FIRST!
i) If brake fluid should come into contact with the skin or eyes, rinse immediately with plenty of water. ii) The brake fluid level will fall slightly during normal use, but if it falls significantly, stop using the vehicle and seek specialist advice. iii) If you get dirt into the hydraulic system it can cause brake failure. Wipe the filler cap clean before removing. iv) Use only new brake fluid from an air-tight container. Old fluid will absorb moisture and this could cause the brakes to fail when carrying out an emergency stop or other heavy use of the brakes - just when you need them most and are least able to do anything about it, in fact!

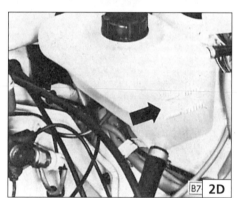

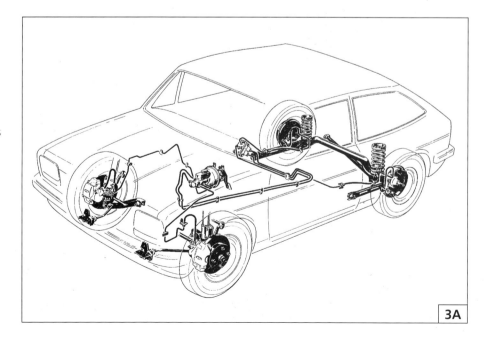

3A. Check/top-up brake fluid level as required.

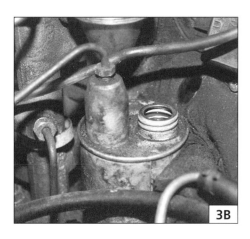

3B. On older cars, the brake fluid reservoir fluid level should be up to the bottom of the filler neck.

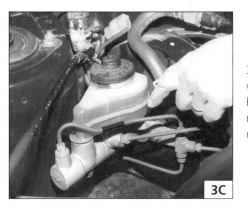

3C. On modern cars, look for a separate plastic reservoir, and usually the assembly will be in unison with the brake servo unit at the back of the engine bay. See your handbook for details. There should be a recommended level mark scribed on the reservoir, which is normally translucent so you can see whether the fluid is up to the mark without having to remove the cap.

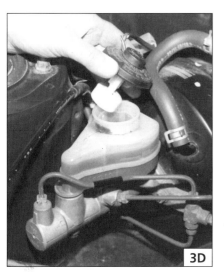

3D. If you do need to remove the reservoir cap on a modern system, note that it may have electrical connections to it and a float or valve beneath the cap. This is the switch mechanism to the 'low fluid' warning lamp found inside the car. Be careful not to damage or accidentally disconnect the wiring.

3E. Top up only with approved brake/clutch hydraulic fluid, fresh from a newly opened container, and have rag handy to catch any accidental spillage - apart from the mess, brake fluid is an excellent paint stripper!

Some reservoirs (like the old car example shown earlier) are so awkwardly positioned that spillage is almost unavoidable!

Note that on disc-braked cars there will be a small, gradual drop in the fluid level over a lengthy period. This is because, as the disc pads' friction material wears, the pad backing plates move nearer to the disc, the brake caliper pistons, in contact with the backing plates, move further out of their bores, the fluid follows the pistons, and more fluid from the reservoir flows into the system to fill the extra space thus created.

SAFETY FIRST!
Should the fluid level drop quite markedly over a short period, the cause must be investigated immediately - it could be dangerous to drive the car until the fault is found and rectified. Although modern dual-circuit hydraulic brake systems should retain some braking ability provided any leakage is confined to just one of the circuits, leakage in an earlier single-circuit system could threaten sudden and total brake failure.

4

☐ **Job 4. Clutch fluid level.**

4. Many cars have a simple cable release mechanism, but you will also find some with a hydraulic system. If your car has a modern hydraulic clutch system, look for a similar master cylinder and reservoir as for the brakes, but without the servo. Topping-up procedure is the same and the same hydraulic fluid is used.

☐ **Job 5. Battery electrolyte.**

SAFETY FIRST!
i) The gas given off by a battery is higly explosive. Never smoke, use a naked flame or allow a spark to occur in the battery compartment. Never disconnect the battery (it can cause sparking) with the battery caps removed. ii) Batteries contain sulphuric acid. If the acid comes into contact with the skin or eyes, wash immediately with copious amounts of cold water and seek medical advice. iii) Do not check the battery levels within half an hour of the battery being charged with a battery charger. The addition of fresh water could then cause the highly acid and corrosive electrolyte to flood out of the battery.

Where the battery is provided with screw caps to the individual cells, or obviously removable strips which plug into or over a number of cells at a time, it is obviously intended that its electrolyte content should be topped up as and when required. But note that even a so-called 'maintenance-free' battery may have flush-fitting strips over its cells which can be prised up for the addition of electrolyte, perhaps prolonging its life beyond general expectation!

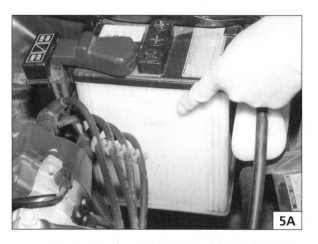

5A

5A. If the battery case is translucent, look for a level mark scribed on its side, otherwise a general recommendation is that the electrolyte level should be just above the tops of the plates which you can see with the cell caps or strips removed.

5B. Some modern batteries have a 'magic eye' which changes colour to indicate the battery's state of charge, or to warn that it is low on fluid.

INSIDE INFORMATION: Note that here is an instance where it is preferable that the battery should be warm, as after a run, before checking the level, since the electrolyte expands with heat. If it were topped up while cold there is a danger that later the fluid would overflow, leading to corrosion of the terminals and accumulated dirt.

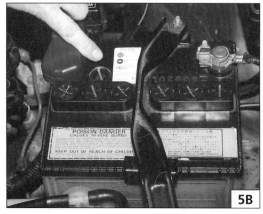

5B

If checking now reveals corroded terminals (typically, a white, powdery growth) refer to 'battery terminals' in the *12,000-mile/12-month service* section.

5C. Top up only with distilled ('de-ionised') water, never ordinary tap water, which may contain impurities which would damage the plates and shorten the battery's life. Mop up any accidental spillage immediately, and make sure the entire battery exterior is clean and dry. You can buy de-ionised water from the auto accessory shop, either in handy top-up bottles or in bulk containers - note that it is highly recommended, too, for steam irons!.

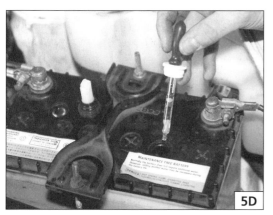

5D. Here's how to check the strength, or specific gravity, of the battery electrolyte. You place the end of a hydrometer into the battery electrolyte, squeeze and release the rubber bulb so that a little of the electrolyte is drawn up into the transparent tube and the float or floats inside the tube (small coloured beads are sometimes used) give the specific gravity. Check each cell and if one (or more) is significantly lower than the others, with battery topped up, the battery is probably on its way out.

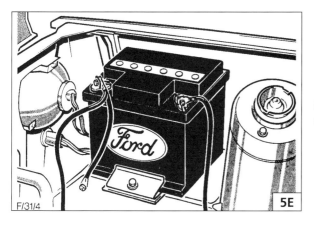

F/31/4

5E. Check the tightness of the battery clamp. A loose, rattling battery will have a shorter life than one that is held down securely.

☐ **Job 6. Screenwash level.**

It can be positively dangerous to run out of screenwash fluid in mid-journey, so check the washer bottle level regularly!

6A. Make sure the reservoir is kept full, using a good brand of screenwash that also promises not to freeze up, and stick to the recommended concentration - never add cooling system antifreeze, since, like brake fluid, this is also an excellent paint stripper!

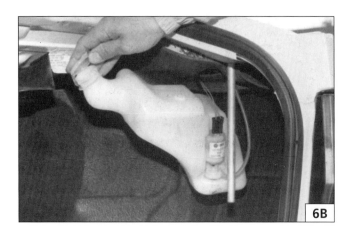

6B. If you have a rear wash-wipe, check whether your car has a separate reservoir, perhaps behind a panel in the boot or hatch.

Around the Car

☐ **Job 7. Tyre pressures.**

This is another job that is best done 'cold', for certainly after any appreciable run the tyres will have warmed up and the air inside will have expanded, giving you a higher pressure reading.

7. Garage airline readings can be unreliable, so use a good quality gauge of your own to check that the tyre pressures accord with your handbook recommendations. Provided the garage is little more than 'just down the road', you can drive there to use the airline, checking afterwards with your own gauge that you have got the pressures right. Of course, having your own footpump, of a good make, is also a good idea! Observe the utmost cleanliness, and don't forget to replace the valve caps afterwards.

☐ **Job 8. Check headlamps and rear lights.**

SPECIALIST SERVICE: It is not possible to set headlamps accurately at home. They will need to be checked by a garage with proper headlamp beam setting equipment.

8A. If you need to change a headlamp bulb, your handbook might be more specific, but this fitting on a Ford Fiesta is fairly typical. Here, working from within the engine compartment, behind the headlamp unit, you first pull off the terminal block which plugs onto the blade pins of the bulb. You then pull away the protective rubber boot, lift the securing spring arms from their slots, and withdraw the bulb. When fitting the new, you'll find that it will sit happily only in one position, steadied by different sized cut-outs and lugs.

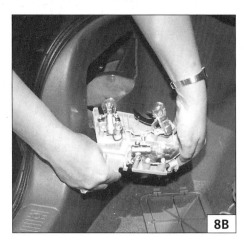

8B. Access to such as the tail lamp, stop lamp (or brake lamp) and direction indicator bulbs of modern car rear light clusters varies. On this Toyota you remove a 'trap door' in the trim panel, then ease away spring clips to allow withdrawal of the bulb cluster.

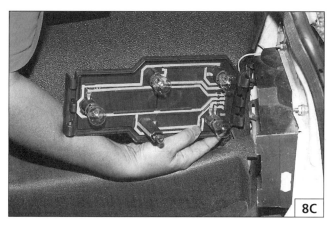

8C. On this Montego, there is a simpler 'plug-in' cluster panel.

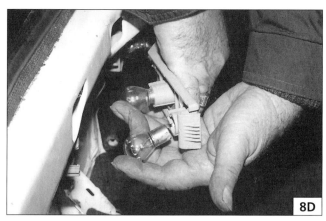

8D. And a not dissimilar set-up on this Ford Escort.

8E. Typical of older cars is this MG Midget, where access to the bulbs is gained by first unscrewing the lens unit - Minis and many others will be similar.

Note that some bulbs, typically a single one serving as both a brake lamp and a tail lamp (packaged as 'stop/tail') have twin lighting filaments and two contact 'pips' on their ends - the staggered locating pins on the side of the bulb ensure that it can only be fitted in its correct position.

(Incidentally, we allowed our lady 'model' to retain her jewelry during this picture session, but generally speaking, and certainly if working in the engine compartment, rings and watches should be removed).

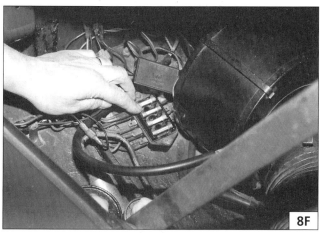

8F. If the bulb of a 'failed lamp' proves to be sound, the problem may be a 'blown' fuse, in which case a whole set of other electrical components may stop working at the same time. If you have a blown fuse (you'll need your handbook to tell you which is which), on an older vehicle the fuse will probably be a strip-type, with the fuse wire either enclosed in a metal-capped glass tube (as here) or the wire could be exposed, wrapped round a ceramic strip. Either type is simply held by spring clips in the 'fuse box'. Once again, look in your handbook to see where the makers have hidden it.

8G. A more modern type of fuse is the plug-in 'blade' type, as shown here. You can buy replacements from any auto accessory store.

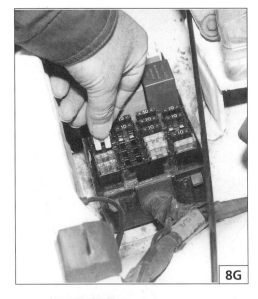
8G

*SAFETY FIRST! If a fuse blows again, after you have replaced it, DON'T be tempted to 'cure' the problem by using a fuse of a higher rating than the one specified or - horror of horrors - using something to bridge the gap where the fuse goes. The fuse will have blown (if more than once) because of an electrical problem. Car fires can start in seconds and are normally **caused** by electrical problems, so have your main dealer or auto-electrician (we recommend the latter, generally), check it out.*

☐ Job 9. Check front indicators.

Check the front indicator bulbs and replace if necessary.

9. INSIDE INFORMATION If an indicator, front, tail, brake or reversing lamp bulb refuses to budge, try gripping it with a piece of cloth or wrapping it with a piece of masking tape - it provides a lot more grip and reduces the risk if the bulb glass breaks. If the bulb comes free of its brass ferrule, disconnect the battery, then carefully break it away and push one side of the ferrule in with a screwdriver. Spray releasing fluid behind the bulb base and leave for a while. Then work the base free by gripping the side that you have pushed in, using a pair of pliers.

9

☐ Job 10. Number plate lights.

Check the rear number plate lights, replacing bulbs if necessary. Note that if two bulbs are fitted, both must work - otherwise it's an 'offence', and an MOT failure!

☐ Job 11. Reversing and foglamps.

Check the reversing lamps, replacing bulbs if necessary. Also check any auxiliary lights, such as foglamps, that may have been fitted as original equipment or as accessories, in which case they are still supposed to function correctly, by law. Original equipment auxiliary lamp bulbs may well be fitted as part of the tail-lamp cluster, as described in Job 8.

☐ Job 12. Clean lamp lenses

Even if the bulbs are sound, light output will be seriously reduced if the lamp lenses are dirty and, again, this is an offence. On a long, 'dirty' journey, you should stop whenever possible and wipe the lenses clean.

☐ Job 13. Check horns.

13. Try the horn button. If the horns fail to work, examine the wiring to the horns themselves.

SPECIALIST SERVICE Horn wiring and connections are more complex than they appear at first. For instance, both terminals at the horn should be 'live'! If there is no obvious problem with the wiring connections, have the horn circuitry and switches checked over by a specialist.

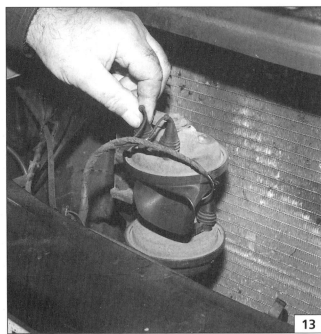
13

15A

☐ Job 14. Check windscreen wipers.

Check that the wiper blades are not torn, worn or damaged in any way. Give each blade a wipe clean with methylated spirit (industrial alcohol). If renewal is required, refer to Job 59 in the *6000 mile/6 month service* section.

☐ Job 15. Windscreen washer/jets.

15A. If the spray from one of the screenwash jets seems uncertain or is non-existent, and you're sure the feed tube to the jet is secure, try poking the jet with a pin to clear possible blockage. Note that on 'ball' type jets, you can use the pin also to swivel the jet to adjust both vertical and lateral aim.

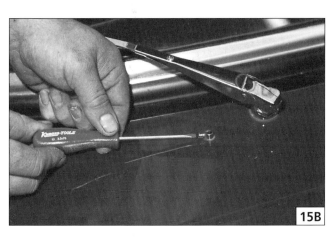

15B

15B. Other types may have a slot in the jet head so you can use a screwdriver blade to adjust the vertical aim, while you may need a small spanner on the jet base to alter lateral aim.

1,500 MILES - OR EVERY MONTH

Around the Car

16A

☐ Job 16. Check tyres.

16A. Check the tyres for tread depth, using a tread depth gauge and note that in the UK, the minimum legal tread depth is 1.6mm. However, tyres are not at their safest at that level, particularly in the wet, and you might want to replace them earlier.

16B. Also check *both sides* of each tyre for uneven wear, cuts, bulges or other damage in the tyre walls. Support each wheel off the ground, using an axle stand, otherwise you won't be able to see the inside of each tyre properly and nor will you be able to check that part of the tread that is in contact with the ground. This tyre is showing lots of minor cracking on the side wall and should be replaced.

INSIDE INFORMATION: Tyres that show uneven wear tell their own story, if only you know how to speak the language! If any tyre is worn more on one side than another, consult your local tyre specialist. It probably means that your suspension or steering is out of adjustment - possibly a simple tracking job but conceivably symptomatic of suspension damage, so have it checked. If a tyre is worn more in the centre or on the edges, it could mean that your tyre pressures are wrong, but once again, have the car checked.

☐ **Job 17. Check spare tyre.**

Check the tread depth, check for damage, the wear pattern and the tyre pressure on the spare wheel, too. You should inflate the spare to the maximum recommended for high speed or high load running. Then, if you have a puncture whilst on a journey, you'll be okay. It's always easier to carry a tyre pressure gauge with you and let some air out than put some in!

Around The Car

☐ **Job. 18. Wash bodywork.**

18A. Wash paintwork, chrome and glass with water and a suitable car wash detergent, taking care not to get 'wax-wash' on the glass - the luxury of a power-wash really speeds the work, and is ideal for Job 23!

18B. Finish by washing the wheels and tyre walls. Leather the paintwork dry.

Use a separate leather on the glass to avoid transfer of polish from paintwork.

☐ **Job 19. Touch-up paintwork.**

Treat stone chips or scratches to prevent or eliminate rust. Allow ample time for new paint to harden before applying polish.

☐ **Job 20. Aerial/antenna.**

Clean the sections of an extending, chrome plated aerial mast. Wipe a little releasing fluid (not oil - it will attract dirt) onto the surface and work in and out a few times.

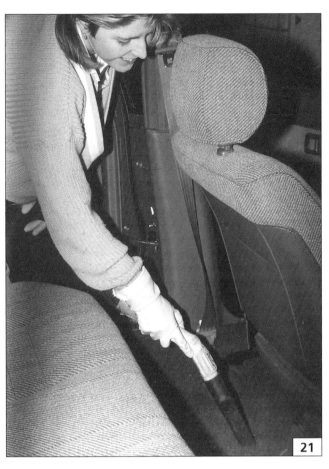

☐ **Job 21. Valet interior.**

21. Use a vacuum cleaner to remove dust and grit from the interior trim and carpets. Those cheap 12 volt vacuum cleaners are generally a waste of money so if you can't get your domestic cleaner to the car, take the car to a garage with a self-service valeting facility. Proprietary upholstery and trim cleaners (interior shampoo) can be surprisingly effective and well worthwhile if the interior has become particularly grubby. Very bad stains, caused by grease, chocolate or unidentified flying brown stuff are best loosened with white or methylated spirit before bringing on the upholstery cleaner - but first test a bit of upholstery that you can't normally see, just in case either of the spirits removes upholstery colour.

Don't forget the under-bonnet, particularly if you have inherited a grimy second-hand buy. A clean engine is nicer to maintain, and the onset of oil or coolant leaks is more easily spotted.

Seat belts should be washed only with warm water and a non-detergent soap. Allow them to dry naturally and do not let them retract, if they're the inertia reel type, until completely dry.

☐ **Job 22. Improve visibility!**

Use a proprietary brand of windscreen cleaner to remove built-up traffic film and air-borne contaminants from the windscreen.

Under the Car

☐ **Job 23. Clean mud traps.**

23A. Hose the underside of the car (if particularly muddy) and allow to dry before putting in the garage, or scrape off dry mud. Wear gloves because mud can force itself painfully behind finger nails!

23B. Clean out the main mud traps behind the headlights and under the wings. This shot shows a favourite gathering point for mud, which holds in moisture and salt and, of course, causes corrosion in a big way!

3000 MILES - OR EVERY THREE MONTHS, whichever comes first

The Engine Bay

☐ **Job 24. Generator drive belt.**

SAFETY FIRST!
Always keep your fingers away from the blades of a thermo-electric cooling system fan unless the battery has been disconnected - it could surprise you by coming on suddenly when the engine is running, and there are some which are not ignition circuit controlled and which will certainly surprise you by coming on (perhaps soon after parking up) when the engine has been switched off!

24A

Still often referred to as the 'fan belt' because on older cars it drove the mechanical cooling fan (usually attached to the water pump) as well as the generator (a dynamo or, later, an alternator) this drive belt continues to be a vital component. On a modern car, while the fan is usually thermostatically controlled and driven by an electric motor, the belt probably still drives the water pump, as well as the alternator. If it slips, or breaks, the car will soon grind to a halt having run out of electricity or overheated, or both.

In order to drive efficiently, as well as being in good condition the belt must be reasonably tight - but not over-tight - around the drive pulleys. Look on the inside of the belt for a shiny surface, cracks or oil; look at the edges for fraying. Replace if there are any problems.

24A. Checking belt condition can be awkward, both from the point of view of restricted access and the difficulty of seeing enough of it in its fitted state: you really need to be able to rotate the engine (ignition off) using a spanner on the alternator or crankshaft pulley nut, bending and twisting each newly exposed length of belt to show up cracks or other damage.

24B

For the belt tension check, a typical recommendation is that there should be approximately 10 mm (1/2 in.) deflection, but check with your car's handbook. Do not overdo the belt tension, for this puts undue strain on the generator and water pump bearings.

24B. Test with firm thumb pressure midway on the belt's longest run between pulleys.

24C. If adjustment is required, the generator pivot bolt(s) and slotted adjustment strap bolts, on engine and generator, need to be slackened. The generator is then pivoted away from the engine until the belt is sufficiently taut, and the bolts then re-tightened.

24D. If necessary, a suitable piece of wood can be used, carefully, as a lever between the engine and the generator drive end bracket to maintain the belt tension while the bolts are tightened.

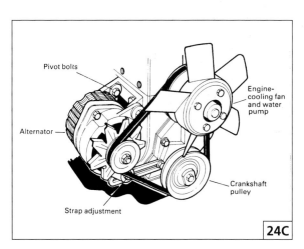

Pivot bolts

Engine-cooling fan and water pump

Alternator

Crankshaft pulley

Strap adjustment

24C

24D

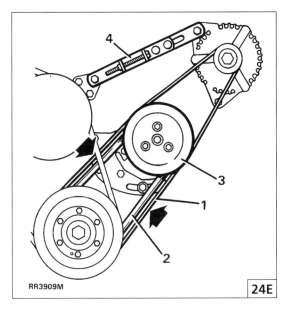

RR3909M | 24E

24E. Very occasionally, you may come across a simple threaded rod and bracket tension adjustment (24E.4). Simply tighten or undo the rod, as required.

INSIDE INFORMATION: In view of this drive belt's vital importance, you should always carry a spare and the right sized spanners to slacken the adjustment bolts: if, even when the generator is pushed tight to the engine, the new belt is difficult to get over the pulleys, follow the old bicycle chain and sprocket trick - push as much of the belt as possible onto the edge of the final pulley, then rotate this pulley to wind the rest of the belt into place.

25

☐ Job 25. Carb dashpots.

Rarely found these days, unless you have a 'golden oldie', but some carburettors (notably the SU which prevailed on so many older cars) have a 'dashpot' (suction chamber) which needs regular topping-up with oil for the jet/piston damper. The damper's job is to allow quick throttle response, but at the same time keep it smooth.

25. Unscrew and remove the damper, then top up (if required) until the oil level is roughly half-an-inch from the top of the hollow piston rod.

Use either clean engine oil (nothing heavier) or an oil sold especially for the job.

26A

☐ Job 26. Check brake/fuel lines.

Examine all the pipe-work for signs of rust or weeping unions - severe rust or even the tiniest of leaks render the car dangerous to drive, and the problems must be rectified immediately.

26A. Regular spraying of metal pipe-work with something like Castrol's DWF helps to keep rust at bay.

26B. Bend flexible brake hoses to show up signs of cracking - if any are found, the hose must be renewed immediately. They must also be free from bulges or oil contamination.

INSIDE INFORMATION: Bend double, especially near the pipe ends and check visually. Also have an assistant press hard on the brake pedal and check for bulging. TAKE NOTE of the Safety First! information on working beneath the car in Chapter 1, Safety First!

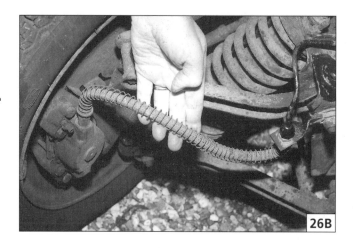

26B

Around the Car

☐ **Job 27. Pipes and hoses.**

Carry out a visual check on all flexible and rigid pipes and hoses in and around the engine bay for leaks.

☐ **Job 28. Check handbrake adjustment.**

This is another job reckoned on older car schedules to need doing at 3000-mile intervals, while latterly it has been deferred to 6000-mile intervals.

Typically, it is expected that the handbrake should be hard on at somewhere between three and five clicks of the ratchet as you pull up the lever.

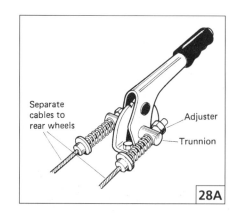

28A

28A. If the lever travel seems over-long, and the result rather ineffective, possibly the handbrake cable has stretched. Look for adjustment (generally a threaded section of the cable with nut and locknut) either at the base of the handbrake inside the car (where the cable or cables attach to the lever) or...

28B. ...beneath the floor, possibly where a single cable from the handbrake lever joins a yoke which then carries two lengths of another cable, one length to each rear brake.

IMPORTANT NOTE: It might be wise to also refer to the 6000-mile attention to the main braking system, since the handbrake should only be adjusted once you are certain that the brakes are correctly adjusted at the wheels.

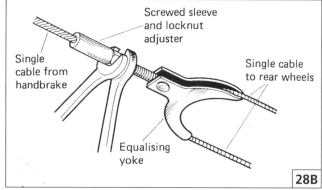

28B

☐ **Job 29. Door and tailgate seals.**

29. To preserve the life and weather-protection efficiency of door and tailgate (or bootlid) seals, they should be cleaned regularly and occasionally be treated with a proprietary 'conditioning' product. Treat sunroof seals similarly.

☐ **Job 30. Check windscreen.**

Check the windscreen for chips, cracks or other damage - see *Chapter 7, Getting Through The MOT* for what is and is not acceptable according to UK regulations.

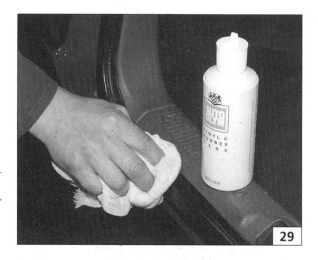

29

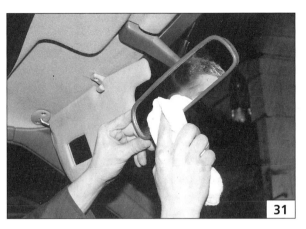

☐ **Job 31. Rear view mirrors.**

Check your rear view mirrors, both inside and outside the car, for cracks and crazing. Also ensure that the interior rear view mirror is soundly fixed in place since they can come loose and when they do, the vibration can get so bad that you can't tell whether you're being followed by a long distance truck or one of the boys in blue!

31. It may sound silly, but it helps if you also keep the mirror glass clean.

☐ **Job 32. Wash and wax the bodywork.**

Wash the bodywork as described earlier then, using a quality car wax, follow the instructions taking care not to get the wax on the windscreen or other glass.

Under the Car

☐ **Job 33. Check exhaust system.**

SAFETY FIRST!
Never run your car's engine in an enclosed space, only ever out of doors.

33. Exhaust gases can be toxic and an exhaust leak can allow gases into the car as you drive along. Check the condition and security of the entire exhaust system, looking carefully for any signs of corrosion on the pipes and silencers, or leakage at the joints. Replace gaskets if necessary. Also, check the condition of all the exhaust mountings.

INSIDE INFORMATION: If you suspect a leak but its location isn't obvious, start the engine and try pressurising the system by holding a piece of board or something similar so that it blocks off the tailpipe - under pressure, the leak should become more noisy, enabling you to track it down. Get an assistant to help if you can, but remember an exhaust system gets extremely hot - neither of you should actually touch the pipe-work anywhere, or you risk a severe burn.

☐ **Job 34. Check steering rack gaiters.**

Most fairly modern cars will have a steering rack, rather than the old-fashioned steering box. Generally speaking, its simpler linkage from steering wheel to road wheels provides quicker, more direct steering response than does the more tortuous multi-lever steering box set-up.

Where each steering rod (or track rod) emerges from each end of the rack unit there will be a convoluted rubber gaiter - sometimes also called a 'boot'. The gaiter stretches or contracts to allow the 'push-pull' movement of the steering rod, but its real job is to keep the rack lubricant in - and the dirt out!

Obviously, this continual movement, plus attack by flying grit from the road surface, can lead to splits in the gaiter: lubricant gets out, abrasive dirt gets in, and very soon the rack mechanism is prematurely worn out.

34. Check for splits very carefully, turning the steering wheel back and forth to stretch the convolutions; check that each end of the gaiter is secure.

Job 35. Track rod ends.

35. Check the rubber boot on each track rod end (TRE). If torn, renew the complete track rod end. In theory, you can replace the boot but it's a false economy for the following reasons. i) Chances are that the old TRE will be worn because the boot has split and because of the resulting absence of lubricant, and ii) the TRE has to be removed from the steering arm in any case. This can be such a devil of a job to carry out that you might as well get it over with and fit a relatively inexpensive, new TRE whilst you're at it.

SPECIALIST SERVICE. This is a tricky job for an inexperienced mechanic to carry out!

35

Job 36. Check drive-shaft gaiters.

Generally speaking, we're talking front-wheel drive, but rear engine, rear-wheel drive will be the same: the joints on the shafts that transmit the drive from the engine (transmission unit) to the road wheels have to allow for suspension movement and (front-wheel drive) steering movement. The gaiters fitted to each end of these shafts have to do much the same job as those on the steering rack, but lead an even more arduous life.

36. Rotate the wheels and turn the steering from lock to lock to check them thoroughly.

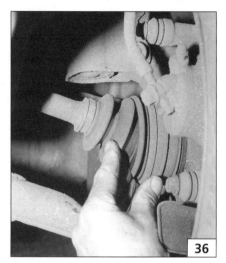
36

Job 37. Grease points.

Unless, again, you have a golden oldie, you might be hard put to find a grease point on any cars these days. The steering and suspension joints, the water pump bearings (typical application points) no longer sprout grease nipples, they are all pre-packed with grease and 'sealed for life'. Initially, there was some cynicism as to how long was 'life', but it has to be said that nowadays these components do seem to last remarkably well.

Even with 'greasable' cars, whereas older ones schedule the operation at this 3000-mile mark, later models (e.g., the Mini) have extended the job to 6000-mile intervals. Generally, we're talking front suspension and maybe steering joints, although the Mini also has nipples on the radius arm bearings of its rear suspension.

37A. Clean off the grease nipple (you don't want to pump dirt into the joint, along with the grease) before pushing the grease gun nozzle onto the nipple. Points to bear in mind are that you might need to swivel the gun nozzle to keep it squarely in line with the nipple and you also need to work out the best avenue of approach - the nozzle will lock on to the nipple, and to unlock and pull away you'll probably need enough room to turn the whole grease gun through nearly a right-angle.

37A

Generally speaking, three or four 'pumps' on the grease gun should be enough. You'll get used to the 'feel' if grease is entering the joint satisfactorily and, indeed, you might hear or see some old grease escaping (forced out by the new). Clean surplus grease away thoroughly.

If things don't feel right and, indeed, the only grease escaping is new stuff spurting between nipple and nozzle, there are a couple of tricks you can try:

37B. First is the old motorist's ploy of interposing a piece of clean lint-free rag between the nipple and nozzle - very often this will effect a seal and work the oracle. If it doesn't, maybe the nipple is blocked with hardened old grease: unscrewing it and holding it in the bench vice while you apply the gun may give you a better chance of clearing it; you can carefully poke it with a piece of stiff wire, but not too forcefully, lest you also poke out the nipple's sealing ball and spring. Better still, go out and buy a new grease nipple from your local motorists' accessory store: they only cost pence!

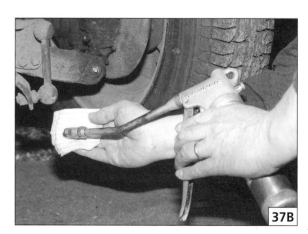
37B

In some cases it might be advantageous to raise the car, allowing wheels and suspension to hang free, whereupon the grease may enter joints more readily. Also, of course, access may be improved, the more so sometimes when a wheel is swivelled from one lock to another.

☐ Job 38. Inspect for leaks.

While under the car, look out for fluid leaks, such as hydraulic fluid spotted on a tyre wall, or oil dripping from beneath the engine or transmission. It is better to spot such leaks early, before danger threatens, or major expense occurs.

Road Test

☐ Job 39. Clean controls.

Clean the door handles, controls and steering wheel: they may well have become greasy from your hands while you were carrying out the rest of the service work on your car. Start up the engine while you are sitting in the driver's seat.

40

☐ Job 40. Check instruments.

40. Before pulling away, and with the engine running, check the correct function of all instruments and switches.

☐ Job 41. Throttle pedal.

Check the throttle pedal for smooth operation. If the throttle does not operate smoothly, turn off the engine and check the cable itself for: a cracked or broken casing, kinks in the casing, or fraying at the cable ends, especially where the ends of the cable 'disappear' into the cable 'outer'. If you find any of these faults, replace the throttle cable.

☐ Job 42. Handbrake function.

Check the function of the handbrake as described under Job 28. But this time, add a further check. An experienced mechanic will be able to engage first gear and let in the clutch just a little at a time until the clutch 'bites' and strains against the hand brake - not too much; just enough to let him know that the brakes are working, and without travelling more than three or four feet (1 metre) or so. If you're not an experienced driver or mechanic and there's some risk that you might strain the car's mechanical components, try turning the engine off, pulling the handbrake on, putting the gearbox in neutral, getting out of the car - only do this on level ground! and see if you can push the car with the handbrake on. If, in the first test, the car moves blithely away, unhindered by the effect of the handbrake, or in the second, if the car moves **at all,** you've got major problems with the rear brakes. The most likely reason is that the brakes are 'oiled' because a brake hydraulic wheel cylinder is leaking brake fluid onto the brake shoes. This requires **SPECIALIST SERVICE,** unless you are an experienced mechanic. THE CAR SHOULD NOT BE DRIVEN until repairs have been carried out.

☐ Job 43. Brakes and steering.

SAFETY FIRST! Only carry out the following tests in daylight, in clear dry conditions when there are no other road users about and no pedestrians. Use your mirrors and make sure that there is no traffic following you when carrying out the following brake tests.

Only a proper brake tester at an MoT testing station will be able to check the operation of the brakes accurately enough for the MoT test, but you can rule out one of the worst braking problems in the following way: drive along a clear stretch of road and, gripping the steering wheel fairly tightly between the thumb and fingers of each hand, brake gently from a speed of about 40 mph. Ideally, the car should pull up in a dead straight line without pulling to one side or the other. If the car pulls to the left (when being driven on the left-hand side of the road) or to the right (when being driven on the right-hand side of the road, such as in the USA), it might be that there is no problem with your brakes but that the camber on the road is causing the car to pull over. If you can find a stretch of road with no camber whatsoever, you may be able to try the brake test again or failing that, find a one-way-street where you can drive on the 'wrong' side of the road and see if pulling to one side happens in the opposite direction. If it does not, then you've got a problem with your brakes. Before assuming the worst, check your tyre pressures; try switching the front wheels and tyres from one side of the car to the other. If after carrying out these modifications in turn, the problem doesn't go away, seek **SPECIALIST SERVICE**.

The second test is to ensure that the self-centring effect on the steering works correctly. If the steering stiffens up over a period of time, you can easily get used to it so that you don't notice that it doesn't operate as it should. After going round a sharp bend, the steering should tend to move back to the straight-ahead position all by itself without having to be positively steered back to the straight-ahead position again by the driver. This is because the swivel pins are set slightly ahead of the centre line of the wheels so that the front wheels behave rather like those on a supermarket trolley - or at least those that work properly! If the swivel pins have become stiff internally because of rust or if new ones have been fitted badly, the steering will be stiff and no self centring will be evident. Drive round a sharp bend and, as you come out of the bend, you should feel the steering wheel tend to turn itself back to the straight-ahead position. If it doesn't and you have to pull the wheel back to the straight-ahead, you've got a problem with the steering and should seek a little more of that **SPECIALIST SERVICE**, unless you're an experienced mechanic and feel capable of diagnosing and rectifying problems with the swivel pins, using your workshop manual.

Now, if you're ready to begin the road test proper, you can check the function of the brakes and the self-centring effect of the steering.

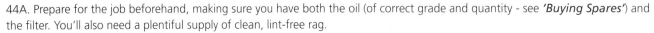

6000-mile/6-month Service

Under the Car

Carry out the 3000-mile/3-month service operations, plus the following:

☐ Job 44. Change engine oil/oil filter.

Probably the one service operation on which most DIY motorists will 'cut their teeth' is an engine oil change - that is emptying the old oil out through the sump drain plug situated beneath the engine and, eventually, pouring in a specified quantity of new oil through the oil filler, usually found on the valve cover at the top of the engine. And no matter how technically complex the engine, an oil change still remains basically a simple operation.

Usually at the same time the engine oil filter will also be renewed, although some service schedules may stipulate that the filter needs to be changed only at every other oil change.

44A. Prepare for the job beforehand, making sure you have both the oil (of correct grade and quantity - see *'Buying Spares'*) and the filter. You'll also need a plentiful supply of clean, lint-free rag.

Make sure you have a suitable receptacle into which the oil can be drained: a washing-up bowl would do, but it has to have enough capacity to hold the contents of the sump and, if you're going to be able to work without having to raise the car, note that the bowl needs to be shallow enough to fit comfortably underneath the engine.

44B. Check whether the sump plug has a hexagon head which can be undone with a conventional ring spanner, or whether (perhaps recessed) it requires a special drain plug key. Do not attempt to 'make do' or you risk 'rounding' the drain plug, making it extremely difficult to grip with any tool.

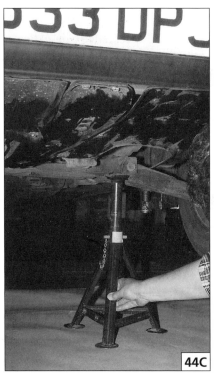

44C. If you are going to have to raise the car to obtain sufficient working room, it will (as stressed earlier) need to be supported securely on ramps or axle stands: make sure you have these to hand. And, having raised the front, will this (beneficially) tip the sump contents towards the drain plug, or away from it, meaning the rear will have to be raised as well?

When all preparations have been made, note that the best time to

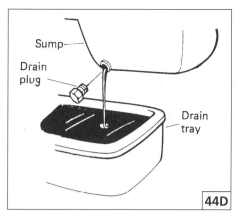

Sump

Drain plug

Drain tray

44D

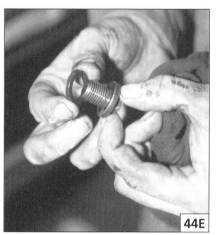

44E

44F

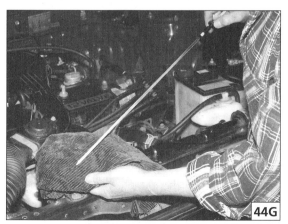

44G

actually drain the oil is after a short drive, when the oil will be warm and will flow more easily.

Before undoing the drain plug, take off the oil filler cap: this relieves any partial vacuum in the system - the faster the oil can drain from the sump the more debris it will drag out with it.

INSIDE INFORMATION: If the drain plug is fitted into the side of the sump, bear in mind that the initial spurt of draining oil may carry some distance sideways - position the drain tray (or bowl) accordingly, being ready to move it inwards as the spurt wanes and the oil falls vertically.

44D. Undo the last few turns of the drain plug by hand, giving yourself room to withdraw hand and plug quickly before (as usually happens, anyway!) the oil runs under your sleeve and all down your arm. Incidentally, check, by feeling the sump, that your short drive hasn't made the oil too hot to handle. Don't take any risks, let it cool a bit.

If the drain plug falls into the bowl (as also often happens) don't worry, you can retrieve it later. When you do, clean it up thoroughly and (if it's not a taper-seal type) check whether its sealing washer is sound, or whether (perhaps looking rather flattened and battered) it needs renewing. Note, too, that where the engine oil also serves the transmission (as is the case with the venerable Mini) there may be a 'magnetic' drain plug fitted: when you remove it may appear to be sprouting whiskers - don't worry, it has simply been doing its job of collecting any metallic swarf drifting around in the sump!

When the sump has dripped its last drop, you can then clean up the seating face of the sump drain plug and refit the cleaned-up plug - it should be done up tight, but not 'murdered'.

44E. IMPORTANT: Always fit a new sealing washer to the drain plug buy from your accessory store at the same time you buy your oil.

(If you are going to change the oil filter at the same time as renewing the oil, now refer to Job 45 before continuing.)

44F. Back up top, you can pour in the correct grade and quantity of fresh oil: do so slowly and carefully, for some engines have a nasty habit of 'glug-glugging' and spewing back, leaving oil then running all over your nice clean engine and reaching parts that you, with your piece of rag, cannot!

44G. Having checked that the oil level corresponds with the correct mark on the dipstick, start the engine and run it for a few minutes while you check around (basically at the filter unit and sump plug) for leaks. Satisfied that all is well, switch off and allow time for the oil to settle before re-checking the level, topping up if necessary.

Pour the old oil into an empty can, ready for eventual carriage to your nearest disposal point (probably your local 'tip'). Clean out the drain tray, clean up and put away your tools, dispose of dirty rags, and the empty filter box, etc, and the job's done.

☐ Job 45. Renew oil filter.

While the oil is draining, you can get on with tackling the oil filter. Fitted on the side of the engine somewhere, sometimes low down, sometimes higher up (often pretty inaccessible!) on an old car it might be of the bowl-and-element type and on newer cars a one-piece canister unit.

(For many years, the air-cooled engines of the VW 'Bus' and Beetle simply relied on a strainer fitted in the sump to 'filter' the oil, and on these vehicles you unbolt the strainer and flush it out at each oil change; later examples were fitted with a conventional exterior filter unit).

Before tackling the filter, however, check first that your drain tray extends far enough to catch any oil spillage as it is loosened, and if it isn't place another suitable, small, receptacle beneath.

On the face of it, the throw-away one-piece canister should be the most straightforward to deal with. But often the bowl-and-element type, secured to the engine with a long through-bolt with conventional hexagon head, is the easiest to remove.

45A. With the latter, having unscrewed the through-bolt, you then lift the bowl away, preferably bringing with it the receptacle beneath to contain any dripping oil: the bolt should remain captive within the bowl. Upending the bowl should tip out the old cartridge filter element. Watch out for a metal base plate and spring beneath the element, restraining them should they try to slide down the bolt, although they should, in fact, also be captive.

Discard the old filter element and swill out the bowl with paraffin, using a brush if necessary, then dry the bowl inside and out with clean lint-free cloth.

45B. Inside the box containing your new filter element should also be a narrow rubber sealing ring: this relates to the trickiest bit as far as this type of filter is concerned. You'll probably find it still stuck in a groove in the filter head on the engine, (the part to which the bowl was bolted) - it has to be carefully prised out with such as the point of a dart or a slim screwdriver blade.

Once it's out (and it's usually pretty inaccessible or at least difficult to see!) make sure the groove and the face of the filter head are thoroughly clean and dry.

Now, bearing in mind how well stuck in was the old seal, you'll be surprised how difficult it can be to get the new seal to stay in place while you offer up the bowl and new filter, working against spring pressure to ensure the narrow rim of the bowl is seated evenly on the seal while you screw in and partially tighten the through-bolt.

Smearing the seal with grease before positioning it will help to retain it, but you must make sure now that it hasn't 'escaped' anywhere before you fully tighten up the bowl - tight, but not 'murdered', by the way.

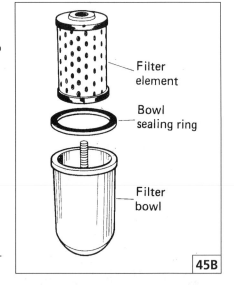

Filter element

Bowl sealing ring

Filter bowl

45C. So really the modern screw-on, screw-off, throw-away canister oil filter should be a much easier proposition. Well it is - provided you can unscrew it! Although when fitted it is (or should be) only screwed on hand-tight, it is amazing how tightly it sets in service. The problem is compounded when, as is so often the case, the filter is a wee bit inaccessible.

If access is that bad, but you can get your hands to it, one trick that often works is, having wiped the outside thoroughly clean and dry, to wrap abrasive paper tightly around it and then grip the paper.

45D. Hopefully, though, there will be enough room to attack it with one of the various DIY filter straps, or wrenches, that are now on the market.

INSIDE INFORMATION: If all else fails, drive an old screwdriver right through the filter and twist it loose.

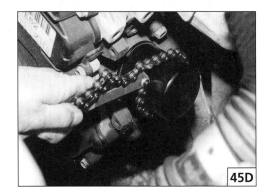

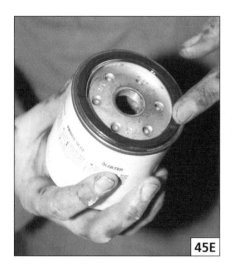

45E. Once off, it's simply a case of cleaning up its mounting point, moistening the captive seal of the new canister with clean oil, then screwing on the new - hand-tight only!

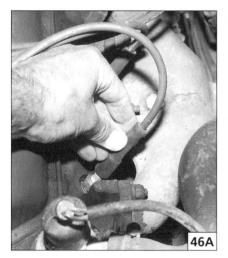

☐ Job 46. Spark plugs.

Generally speaking, most service schedules will suggest that the spark plugs are cleaned and their electrode gaps reset as necessary at 6000-mile intervals and that the plugs are renewed at 12,000-mile intervals unless their condition dictates earlier renewal - see 'Spark Plug Conditions' later in this book.

46A. INSIDE INFORMATION: When detaching plug leads, pull on the plug cap, not on the lead itself - also see our advice on removing and numbering the spark plug HT leads in Job 47.

You will need a proper tubular spark plug removal tool (a sophisticated box spanner) which can be bought as a separate item, although it is normally included in a good quality socket set. It needs to be the correct size for the plugs used by your car (predominately 14mm, but sometimes 10mm thread diameter, with correspondingly larger or smaller bodies). Incidentally, you don't often see the actual spanner size quoted, but they are, respectively, 13/16 in. AF (21 mm) and 5/8 in. (16 mm). The tool should also have a rubber insert which sleeves over the plug's porcelain stem, guarding against this vulnerable part tipping in the spanner and fracturing. Some engines have their plugs buried quite deeply and for these, extra long plug spanners are available.

46B. Note that grime is apt to accumulate around the plug seating, and since much of this could be abrasive you don't want it getting into the cylinders. So, a simple precaution before removing a plug, is to brush away all the surrounding dirt.

46C. Make sure your plug tool or socket is seated squarely and firmly over the plug, so there's no danger of slippage and consequent injury or damage, before applying any leverage - 'taper seat' plugs can set quite tightly and require pretty firm pressure to shift them.

Keep the plugs in cylinder order as you remove them and check their condition. The colouring at the business end of a spark plug in healthy condition was described traditionally as 'chestnut', but brown or greyish and dry are 'OK' symptoms (again, see 'Spark Plug Conditions' later).

Should any plug look decidedly unhealthy, it might be symptomatic of a tiring or failed plug, or it might indicate a fault with the engine, perhaps confined to just the one cylinder - and you know which cylinder because you kept the plugs in order of removal.

46D. If the plugs are definitely fit for further service, use a brass-bristled wire brush to spruce up their business ends, preferably with the electrodes pointing downwards, so debris doesn't enter the plug body: if this becomes unavoidable, blow the dirt out or tap the plug body to dislodge it.

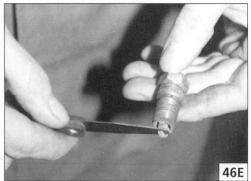

46E. Now check the electrode gaps, bearing in mind that spark erosion widens the gap. Use a feeler gauge of the appropriate value according to the plug gap specified in your car data (e.g., 0.025 in. or '25 thou', or, metrically, 0.60 mm). The dual measurements of an ignition 'contact set' will be useful.

(With modern high-power electronic ignition, you may find much larger gaps than that traditional '25 thou' specified. For instance, on 'our' Toyota Corolla the plug gap is 0.043 in., or 1.1 mm - check your handbook!)

If the gap does need altering, some 'contact set' also contain the tool for the job. The slots in one of their blades can be used (carefully) to lever the plug's side (earth) electrode nearer to, or further from, the central electrode - never attempt to bend this centre electrode.

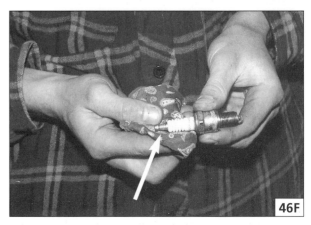

46F. Before replacing the plugs, use pliers to ensure that the terminal nut at the HT lead end is tight (some engines, e.g., VW air-cooled, dispense with this nut) and that the plug stem is clean and dry - dirt here, particularly oily dirt, can encourage the HT current to 'track' to earth rather than continue on to the plug electrodes.

INSIDE INFORMATION: In our experience a smear of copper grease on the (cleaned up) spark plug threads helps them to screw in smoothly now and prevents them setting so tight in service as to make their removal difficult next time. We particularly like the smooth, positive, thread pick-up when dealing with those air-cooled VW engines, where, with the plug held in the tubular spanner, you have to 'feel' for a plug hole you can't see and pray that you don't cross-thread the plug, a potentially expensive nightmare on any aluminium-head engine!

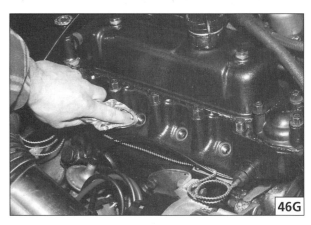

46G. Make sure, using rag and screwdriver blade as necessary, that the actual plug seating is absolutely clean before screwing-in the plug...

46H

47A

46H. ...using your fingers first, then the spanner to initially do it up hand-tight. The 'rule-of-thumb' then is that, using the spanner, plugs with washers should be tightened a further quarter of a turn, and taper-seat plugs a further one-sixteenth of a turn. Check, though, that your car data doesn't quote a specified tightening torque for the plugs in your engine: it is particularly unwise to overdo it with a taper-seat plug, as this could render it practically impossible to remove at the next service.

☐ Job 47. Distributor.

Specifically, the work here concerns attention to (where fitted) the contact-breaker ('CB') points. But at the same time, even if not noted in the schedule, it will be sensible to thoroughly clean the distributor cap inside and out, and to clean the rotor arm and the high-tension (HT) spark plug and coil leads; some distributors also demand periodic lubrication.

Note that dirt or damp inside or outside the distributor cap will encourage the HT current to 'track' to earth, rather than continue on through the HT leads to the spark plug electrodes. The problem will cause misfiring and generally poor engine performance, maybe even a refusal to start. In bad cases the 'tracking' will burn zig-zag lines into the surface of the cap, generally leaving the cap unfit for further service.

47A. Talking of the spark plug HT leads, sooner or later, when servicing the distributor or the spark plugs, you'll need to detach the leads from the plugs. If they are not already numbered according to the cylinders they feed (1, 2, 3, 4, or more) a simple but effective 'aide memoir' is to clip an appropriately numbered clothes' peg to each. Remember from which end of the engine you have started numbering - usually, on an in-line engine No.1 is the radiator end, while on a transverse engine No.1 will be at the water-pump, or drive-belt end. When detaching the lead from the plug, pull on the plug cap, not on the lead itself, as this could be bad for its health.

Returning to the distributor, if your car does have contact-breaker ignition, as opposed to the more modern all-electronic ignition, then the contact-breaker points will need regular attention and eventual renewal.

As implied by the description, the contact-breaker is basically a switch, making and breaking an electrical connection at the 'points'. Put simply, the critical timing and strength of the eventual spark at the spark plug electrodes in the engine are partly governed by the size of the gap between the CB points when they are opened by a 'cam' on the distributor shaft which is driven by the engine: a cam is, in effect, a raised ridge on the shaft, and generally speaking there will be as many cams as there are engine cylinders - e.g., four, six or eight, as far as most cars on the road are concerned.

The size of the points gap required for optimum ignition performance is carefully pre-determined by the car manufacturer and will be specified in the handbook data; or there might instead be a 'dwell angle' specified, which we will come to shortly.

Since the contact-breaker is a mechanical device, wear and tear can eventually alter this gap. At the same time the spark that occurs at the gap when the points open dirties and erodes the points faces, this, too, varying the size of the gap over a period of time. Eventually, the combination of mechanical wear and spark erosion will render the CB points beyond further useful service.

Until they reach this stage, your regular 'service' needs to ensure the points faces are cleaned and that the points gap is adjusted, if necessary, to bring it back to 'spec'.

Something of a set-back for the home mechanic of some years ago, was when some car manufacturers introduced a distributor 'dwell angle' specification, rather than a CB points gap. The dwell angle relates to the rotation of the distributor shaft between cams during the 'dwell period', this being the length of time the points remain closed, while energy builds up in the ignition coil to feed the spark plug when the points open.

(The ignition coil can be identified as the component, always at one time tubular, but not necessarily so these days, to which the HT lead running from the centre of the distributor cap attaches at its other end).

Even if the dwell angle was specified in your handbook, there would be the rider that it could only be measured by special equipment and so, the handbook would add smugly, this was a job you would have to entrust to your authorised dealer!

Fortunately, it wasn't long before the accessory market cottoned on to the fact that to get the correct dwell angle you simply adjusted the points gap to suit - and thus was born the inexpensive DIY 'dwell meter', now often incorporated as one of the functions in the more widely useful 'multi-meter', or 'engine analyser'.

With the dwell meter you can measure the angle yourself and adjust the points until the meter registers the specified 'angle' expressed in degrees, a typical example being set out as 55 plus or minus 5 degrees.

47B. To check this, the leads of your dwell meter (or multi-meter) would be connected between the distributor low tension (LT) terminal, or coil CB (or 'neg') terminal, and earth (chassis). With the engine then started and running at idle, a reading on the dwell scale between 50 and 60 degrees would be within specification.

47B

This method does have the advantage that the measurement is checked while the engine is running, when the meter reading will have taken account of any 'wobble' in the distributor shaft or variations in cam wear: static measurement of a specified points gap with a feeler gauge (unless you re-check on all cam lobes and average out the result) will not have the same accuracy, although in a basically sound system this should not be particularly critical.

However, the 'bane' with dwell angle settings is that, if adjustment is required, on most engines you have to switch off and then remove the distributor cap to make the necessary adjustment, then replace the cap and start up again to re-check the meter reading - we have come across very few examples where the distributor has featured an exterior points adjustment, allowing alterations to the gap with the meter attached and the engine running.

Note that too wide a points gap will give too small a dwell angle, and vice versa.

Earlier, we talked of cleaning and adjustment of the CB points at service periods, until eventually one of the service checks reveals that the time has come to renew the points.

We also mentioned spark 'erosion'. Not strictly accurate, because what usually happens is that a 'pit' is eroded from one contact face and a 'pip' is deposited on the other. Not only does this condition give rise to a false impression of the gap between the points when a feeler gauge is inserted, it is also very difficult to both spot and clean up effectively when the points are in situ.

So we have to admit that when we measure ease of starting and the economy of good performance against the cost of a set of new points, we opt to cut out all the hassle and uncertainty of trying to ensure old points are properly cleaned and gapped by simply fitting a new set at each service!

And even then, when access to the unit 'in situ' is particularly difficult, some home mechanics may well also opt to remove the distributor and renew the points and set the gap on the bench!

This may be a frightening prospect, but need not be if certain simple precautions are first taken.

What must be avoided is losing the ignition timing, by replacing the distributor with either its body or its shaft far removed (in a rotational sense) from their original positions.

Taking the distributor body first, with the cap still on, simply making a note (a sketch would be sensible) of the alignment of some feature on the cap (or body) and of a feature on the engine should ensure you get the body back right: you might be off the original timing by a degree or so, but we will be dealing with ignition timing adjustment later in this section.

As well as having removed the spark plug leads, you'll need also to detach the HT lead that runs from the centre of the distributor cap to the coil: detach it at whichever end is most convenient. The thin low tension (LT) lead perhaps bolted or clipped to the side of the distributor will have to be removed as well; occasionally this LT lead will be more easily disconnected at the coil, but remember which terminal it came from. Also pull off the thin pipe fitted between the carburettor and the distributor vacuum-advance unit.

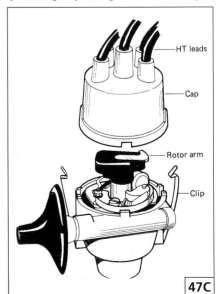

HT leads

Cap

Rotor arm

Clip

47C

47C. Next, remove the distributor cap (see later text) and make a note of the rotor arm position in relation to the distributor body: ideally, the engine should be turned until the business end of the rotor arm points to the electrode in the distributor cap which feeds the HT lead to No.1 spark plug; then, if you like, you can lightly scribe a rotor arm alignment mark on the rim of the distributor body.

We have already talked of removing the cap, and generally this is a simple matter of using your fingers to prise away two spring clips on opposite sides of the distributor; on some units the cap will be secured by two screws, rather than clips.

47D. Sometimes (as on this old Ford Fiesta) the clips are so difficult to get at that you will be better off springing them off the cap with a screwdriver. Hold the lower part with your other hand so the clip doesn't spring right off the distributor!

Make sure you can remember the positioning of the cap on the body, although there should, in fact, be matching cut-outs and notches on cap and body rims that would preclude the cap from fitting properly other than in its correct position.

(On a typical all-electronic ignition system, your service attentions now should go no further than ensuring the cap is thoroughly clean and dry inside and out, and that the HT leads are similarly clean and dry - and, of course, this job should be managed with the distributor still in place on the engine).

INSIDE INFORMATION: If your car's distributor is badly 'hidden', remove it as described below. Otherwise - and whenever possible, carry out this work with the distributor in situ!.

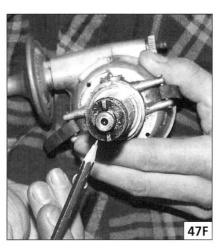

47E. Now slacken off the distributor clamp bolt until it is loose enough to allow the distributor to be pulled from the engine.

DO NOT ROTATE THE ENGINE AGAIN UNTIL AFTER THE DISTRIBUTOR HAS BEEN RE-FITTED!

47F. Look now at the driven (bottom) end of the distributor shaft. More often than not, the driven end (the 'dog') is simply a protruding blade or ridge which is offset to the centre-line of the shaft; this dog mates with a slot, also offset to the centre-line, in the drive remaining within the engine. Common-sense will tell you that, with this offset, the shaft can only be replaced in one position - its original, correct position.

Very occasionally, the driven end will be a toothed gear, which has to mate with a gear drive in the engine. Here it is simply a matter of trial and error of entering the shaft turned back from the alignment you have marked until the twist that occurs as the gears mate actually rotates the shaft to this marked position.

Returning now to the contact-breaker points (distributor in situ or on the bench) we can describe a typical cleaning, renewal or adjustment procedure, but there are occasional variations in points layout, so if yours differs from the main text in any respect it will be wise to make notes or a sketch so you can return parts as you found them.

47G. With a CB points set-up, as mentioned earlier in this text, removing the distributor cap will reveal the rotor arm (the item that passes the high-tension current to each plug lead in turn) sitting on top of the distributor shaft. It is a push fit, with a keyway both to ensure it can only be fitted the correct way round and to stop it moving round other than with the shaft. Beneath the rotor arm, free to be removed once the latter is pulled off, may be a dust shield: it might be pegged to the rim of the distributor body.

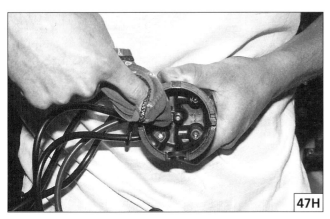

47H. Thoroughly clean the distributor cap inside and out, and also clean the rotor arm.

You are strongly recommended to renew points rather than clean them; they're cheap enough! First note the various thin-wire (low tension) connections. Generally, you'll be looking at two of them, one virtually a continuation of the LT lead from the coil to the side of the distributor, the other a lead from the short, tubular 'condenser' or 'capacitor' unit which is part of the energy system and which is normally mounted on the distributor base-plate.

47I. Secured by a nut, the leads may terminate in tags through which is sleeved a plastic 'top hat' insulator, the latter sleeved in turn into the top of an eye at the end of the moving contact's spring blade.

47J. This assembly, with a matching 'top hat' pushed into the bottom end of the eye, is then also sleeved over a post situated on the fixed contact.

47K. The leads are in connection with the moving contact, but the plastic 'top hat' sleeves insulate both the leads and the moving contact from the fixed contact.

The 'moving contact' has a fibre (or plastic) heel which is pushed by the cams on the distributor shaft, this causing the moving contact to pivot on another, insulated, post on the fixed contact; the effect is to open up the contact faces. The spring blade ensures the points are kept closed when no cam is in contact with that heel.

Variations on the electrical connections include an insulated terminal block on the side of the distributor, with the moving contact's spring blade slotting onto this terminal, or the points set may have an integral lead that pushes onto a blade tag, also at this terminal.

Unbolting this terminal block, or removing the nut, uppermost 'top hat' and the leads from the post described earlier may leave the moving contact free to be lifted away, off its pivot post.

47L. But more likely, given the wide use of modern one-piece contact-breaker sets, it will be captive at the pivot point: undoing the single screw and washers which secure the fixed contact to the base-plate...

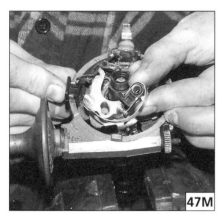

47M. ...will allow both moving and fixed contacts to come away as one piece.

47N. If your maintenance schedule calls for periodic lubrication of the distributor, this is easier once the points have been lifted away (although in this picture they are still fitted). It will usually be suggested that a few drops of oil from an oil can are dribbled into the hollow top of the cam (the oil will seep past the head of the cam securing screw and lubricate the cam bearing at the top of the distributor shaft); also dribble some oil through the base-plate apertures onto the automatic-advance weight mechanism beneath. Put a *very* light smear of grease on the cam faces.

47O. It is also easy now to check the operation of the vacuum-advance unit, although, in fact, we checked ours when the points were reassembled - simply suck on the tube and you should see the base-plate swivel back and forth.

(Both this unit - which is operated by vacuum emanating from the carburettor, or inlet manifold, and the automatic-advance weight unit, where the weights fly out under increasing centrifugal force, by swivelling the base-plate alter the position of the points in relation to the cam - have the effect of 'advancing' the ignition timing when this is advantageous to the engine's needs).

Make sure the base-plate is thoroughly clean now before positioning your new set of points. Note that it can be difficult persuading the securing screw to enter its hole in the base-plate and pick up the thread cleanly. This should be less of a problem if you're working on the bench, but on the car you would be well advised to make sure any apertures in the base-plate large enough for the screw to drop through should it escape are temporarily blocked off with tissue paper. Tighten the screw just sufficiently to nip up the points.

47P. Turn the engine or (on the bench) rotate the distributor shaft until one of the cam lobes is exactly on the heel of the moving contact: this should open the points. If it doesn't, locate the contact set's adjustment point: typically, this will be an arrangement such as a notch in the end of the fixed contact plate, perhaps matching a similar notch or straddling a pip on the base-plate - you'll see that a suitably-sized screwdriver blade inserted in the notch and twisted one way or another, levering between the two notches or between notch and pip, will move the fixed contact and thus open or close the points.

Experiment, if necessary, until you've got the knack and have also found how tight the securing screw needs to be to allow and hold adjustment without the points sliding closed again.

Now you will need a feeler gauge whose thickness matches the specified points gap for your car - typically, again, this would be in the region of 0.016 in. or its metric equivalent (0.40 mm), or "sixteen thou" in., admittedly rather dated, workshop parlance!

Probably a tolerance will be given, e.g., 0.014-0.016 in. (0.35-0.40 mm). You might like to note, by the way, that, although you can buy specifically imperial or metric sets of feeler gauges, the ignition 'contact set' of feelers mentioned earlier will usually have the imperial measurement stamped on one side of the feeler blade and the metric equivalent on the other.

47Q. Anyway, back to the adjustment. Using the screwdriver, adjust the gap until the feeler is a close sliding fit between the points, then tighten the securing screw; re-check the gap, because tightening the screw occasionally upsets the adjustment and you might have to repeat the exercise a few times until you get it dead right.

Incidentally, not only is it much easier on the bench to be absolutely sure that the peak of the cam is exactly on the heel, but it is also only a few minutes' work to re-check the gap on all other cams. Hopefully, there will be very little, if any, variation - otherwise, of course, you have a worn distributor problem.

Provided all is well, replace the distributor if off the car, or simply refit the dust shield, rotor arm and cap, and the job's done.

47Q

☐ Job 48. Ignition timing.

Now that we have got the plugs and points sorted out, we can turn to the ignition timing, checking it or adjusting it as needs be. (Note that with all-electronic ignition the timing should not need checking, since it should never alter unless it has been physically disturbed).

As mentioned within the section dealing with the contact-breaker points, the timing of the sparks at the sparking plug electrodes within the cylinders is critical. There are many factors involved in the determining of when best to 'fire' the fuel mixture in the cylinder for optimum combustion and power. For the engine designer it's a complicated juxtapositioning of pistons, valves and sparks to ensure, for instance, that maximum fuel mixture is drawn into the cylinder on the piston's induction stroke and that the piston is then best placed in the cylinder bore for the 'bang' to send it on its way to maximum effect.

You may recall the petrol engine's 'suck, squeeze, bang, blow' four-stroke cycle - or, more properly, 'induction, compression, ignition, exhaust'. And, of course, actually it's not a 'bang', but rather the expansion of the burning mixture that pushes the piston down on its power ('ignition', or 'firing') stroke.

The specified ignition timing will usually relate simply to the position of the piston in the bore while still on (again, usually) its compression stroke, and will (like the dwell angle) be expressed in degrees - typically, 10 degrees BTDC.

That abbreviation 'BTDC' stands for 'before top dead centre'. So in this example the setting requires that the spark plug electrodes actually 'spark' when the piston is almost at the top of its compression stroke in the cylinder bore - it would require another ten degrees of crankshaft rotation for it to actually reach the top.

(Very occasionally have we come across engines where the setting is 'ATDC' - 'after top dead centre' - when, in effect, the piston has already started downwards on its power stroke).

48A. The 'timing marks' where the setting can be checked are on the engine exterior and typically consist of a pointer, or series of pointers, on the end of the engine adjacent to the crankshaft pulley, and a notch in the rim of that pulley. The pulley notch is (obviously) the moving mark, while the pointer is the fixed mark: if there is more than one pointer, each will normally be inscribed with (in degrees) its value - perhaps '0', '8' and '10', or similar, with '0', when aligned with the pulley notch, indicating (in a typical four-cylinder engine) that a pair of pistons (generally numbers one and four) are at 'TDC', or 'top dead centre'.

(Sometimes the moving mark will be on the engine flywheel, and will be viewed through an aperture in the transmission casing.)

More often than not these days car data will specify 'stroboscopic' (or 'dynamic') rather than 'static' ignition timing. It is a method that (as with the dwell angle) allows the setting to be checked with the engine running so that, again, any looseness in the working parts is accounted for.

The method involves the connection of a stroboscopic ('strobe') light to the plug HT lead of the cylinder used for the timing check - usually number one. With the engine running, the strobe will 'flash' each time power flows through the HT lead - i.e., each time number one's spark plug 'sparks'.

Even at tick-over, the sparks and, therefore, the flashes are so frequent that the light appears to be continuous and when it is pointed at the engine's ignition timing marks it has the effect of 'freezing' the moving mark, so that the latter's relationship with the fixed mark can easily be seen.

If you don't already possess a strobe light, your accessory shop will stock various models at an affordable price. The easiest to use are those with a xenon light (brighter than neon) and an inductive pick-up that simply clamps over the plug's HT lead. Most are simply powered via clip-on leads to the car battery, although there are models that use their own internal batteries.

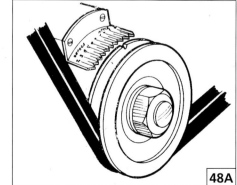

48A

Where there is more than one fixed mark it probably means that the engine serves more than one model in a range of cars, and the setting given in your handbook will determine which pointer (sometimes a 'V' or valley between pointers) should be used on your particular car. If the data gives both a stroboscopic and a static setting, it is the strobe one you want, although just occasionally the same figure will be given for both.

The strobe setting will normally carry with it a rider that it should be checked with the engine running at a particular speed, generally close to normal idling (tick-over) speed, perhaps with a tolerance of 50rpm, and it may well also specify that the vacuum pipe between the carburettor and the distributor should be disconnected from the distributor, so there's no danger of the latter's vacuum-advance unit coming into play and confusing the setting. You may need to plug the pipe temporarily to have the engine continue to run smoothly.

So, a typical data setting would read '10 degrees BTDC at 850 +/- (which means, plus or minus) 50 rpm, vacuum disconnected'. It will help operations now if, having cleaned the timing marks, you pick out both the correct pointer and the pulley notch with a small blob of white paint, or 'Tipp-Ex' is ideal - it should be mentioned, by the way, that often the timing marks will be in some deep, dark, inaccessible area of the engine compartment!

48B

48B. Connect up your strobe, start the engine and check that the idling speed is as specified for the timing check, adjusting it as necessary - if your car doesn't have a rev-counter, here's an example of where a multi-meter can be of assistance. Now point the strobe light at the timing marks, noting how it freezes the moving mark - the more accessible flywheel marks mentioned earlier are easier to photograph! If the correct moving mark aligns with the correct fixed mark, all is well, if it doesn't, adjustment is required.

(Incidentally, having checked earlier, by sucking on the pipe, that the distributor vacuum advance unit was working, you can at this point also check the automatic advance weight mechanism - if the weights are doing their job, simply blipping the throttle should cause those marks to move apart).

To adjust the timing, stop the engine, then loosen the distributor clamp bolt just sufficiently so the distributor can be turned by hand. Note that adjustment is best done with the engine running, so a wise precaution now is to wear a rubber glove, or try to grip just the body of the distributor, rather than the cap, so as to avoid any danger (see earlier warning) of shocks from HT leakage (there shouldn't be any, of course) and also, when reaching for the distributor, beware of moving parts.

Start the engine again, point the strobe at the timing marks, and carefully turn the distributor back and forth - you'll see the moving mark move either closer to, or further away from the fixed mark. Adjust until they align, then stop the engine and tighten the distributor clamp. Start up again and re-check, and if all is well stop the engine once more.

Satisfied the ignition timing is now correct, reconnect the vacuum pipe and if necessary adjust the tick-over back to normal idling speed.

Should your car data allow only for static ignition timing, the procedure for checking it is simple enough.

First you need a 12-volt bulb with two leads attached to it, either via a holder or soldered directly to the bulb.

(Some motorists used to save old twin-filament bulbs, on which only one filament had failed, just for this purpose: one lead would be soldered to the bulb casing, the other to the 'pip' serving the surviving filament).

48C. Connect the bulb between the distributor LT terminal (or coil CB/neg terminal) and earth (chassis). Slacken the distributor clamp bolt as before, and if it's an old design having a Vernier adjuster fitted, this should be on its central setting.

Remove the distributor cap and turn the engine (easiest with the spark plugs removed) until the timing marks are aligned and the rotor arm is pointing towards the segment in the cap which serves number one spark plug HT lead: leave the cap off.

Now switch on the ignition and carefully turn the distributor body in the direction of rotation of the rotor arm. Turn it back again until the bulb lights, which indicates that the CB points have just opened - you should see that the cam peak is precisely on the points heel.

The distributor body should now be properly positioned for correct static timing, but it's worth turning it back and forth a few times to satisfy yourself that you do have the exact point where the bulb lights, before switching off the ignition, tightening the clamp and replacing the cap.

Before replacing the spark plugs, you can double-check the adjustment by (ignition on and bulb connected) turning the engine over a few times, ensuring the timing marks are exactly aligned each time the bulb lights. The real experts can achieve any 'fine tuning' they feel is required after road test by using the Vernier adjustment.

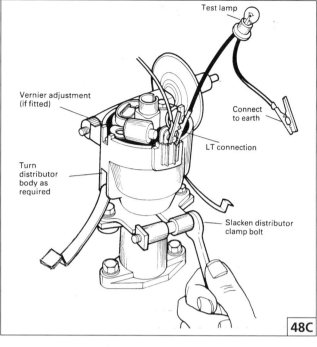

Test lamp

Vernier adjustment (if fitted)

Connect to earth

LT connection

Turn distributor body as required

Slacken distributor clamp bolt

48C

☐ Job 49. Accelerator controls.

49. Lubricate the accelerator control linkage at the carburettor/s and (where applicable) the throttle pedal pivot, in the recesses of the footwell. Use spray-on lubricant or white silicone grease in the footwell, so as not to spoil your shoes with dripping oil - it stains leather!

49

☐ Job 50. Carburettor settings.

SAFETY FIRST!
Please read the Safety information in Chapter 1, especially that relating to the safety hazards surrounding petrol (gasoline). In addition, note that, if twin carburettors need to be balanced, you will have to run the car with the air filter(s) removed. There is the slight risk of a flashback through the carburettor(s), so don't get your face or clothing too close. Also, have a suitable workshop-sized extinguisher to hand, in case the worst should happen. If a fire should break out, turn off the ignition - and thus the engine and fuel pump - immediately so that no more petrol can be pumped through. Because of the fire risk, however slight, and because of the very strong danger from exhaust fumes, carry out the next part of the work out of doors.

Today, of course, the carburettor is largely being phased out in favour of fuel injection systems: the latter not only allow extremely precise metering of the fuel/air mixture, but also can be almost continuously 'adjusted' (along with the ignition timing, even the valve timing on some engines) by electronic wizardry sensing the continuously varying demands of the engine. Even where a carburettor is still fitted, it will be exceedingly complex and finely calibrated to achieve, like the injection system, the maximum economy consistent with high performance, and, of course, the least possible toxic emissions from the exhaust - e.g., carbon monoxide, or 'CO'.

Even if such a carburettor displays any visible potential for adjustment (and for many years now, of course, mixture adjustments have been fitted with supposedly tamper-proof seals) the specific information you really ought to have is beyond the brief of a book such as this. Such clever designs are expected, of course, to cover huge mileages without going out of tune, and it has to be said this is largely the case.

However, while it could be both foolish and unproductive to tamper with them in their early years, on an older car, obviously out of tune, there may be nothing to be lost, but hopefully something to be gained, by tackling them - and the general information in this section pertaining to both older and more recent designs might still be of assistance.

For removing the 'tamper-proof' seals, usually no more than a sharp screwdriver or scissors point should be needed to prise out the plastic or wax plug, or lever off a metal cap.

Beneath the seal will probably be found a conventional screw-head adjuster, or maybe a screw-head needing a twin-pronged 'tool' that you could cobble up from your scrap-box. A carburettor specialist will probably stock any unconventional tool needed.

50A. For getting the idling (tick-over) to accord with the speed specified in your handbook (generally in the region of 800rpm) we have already mentioned the useful 'multi-meter', its RPM (revs per minute) scale a handy under-the-bonnet reference even if your car does have a rev counter (or 'tachometer') among its fascia instruments.

(With cars of yesteryear, where no specific idling speed was listed, you normally adjusted it so that the ignition warning light was just extinguished, and so that it idled smoothly with no attempt to stall in traffic situations. Note, too, that even on a modern car when headlamps and other electrical equipment, particularly screen demisters, are in operation, the load on an alternator demands extra engine power which will slow down the tick-over - switch your headlamps to main beam with the engine idling and you'll hear it slow down!).

50A

Apart from the generally useful multi-meter, many accessory shops will also stock various aids dedicated to carburettor tuning, including devices to help 'balance' multiple carb installations - particularly useful for the twin SU carb set-up used extensively on older cars. There's even a novel glass-topped spark plug ('Colourtune') which enables you to see the burning mixture and which comes with instructions on what 'colour' denotes the ideal mixture, and tells how to adjust to obtain it.

50B. But for really precise mixture setting (and it's a 'must' for cars dating from August 1975, where an emissions test is included in the 'MoT') you really need a 'CO meter' - or 'exhaust gas analyser'. A professional one, as used by the MoT stations, would be way beyond your pocket, but pretty good DIY alternatives are produced by firms such as Gunsons, who also market that 'Colourtune'. That said, even a basic DIY gas analyser (shown in use here) will probably set you back the cost of a couple of tyres, so maybe the answer is to share it (and its cost!) with like-minded motoring friends.

(It needs to be remembered, incidentally, that the level of noxious waste emitted with the exhaust gas is governed very much by the engine's combustion efficiency, not just by the mixture setting at the carburettor, so it is essential that all components of the ignition system are absolutely spot-on before attempting to tune for 'emissions'. It also needs to be remembered that while the subject of emissions tends to be simplified by talking of the 'CO', or carbon monoxide, content, the 'HC', or hydrocarbons, content is also subject to the emissions regulations. The DIY gas analyser will indicate the CO level, but is unlikely to read out the exhaust's HC content. Generally, however, if the ignition is sound and the fuel mixture is right for an acceptable CO reading, then, the HC level will also be within bounds).

Where a modern car's handbook actually quotes a CO figure, it may often be in the region of 2.5%, which is considerably lower than the maximum allowed by those MoT regulations current as we go to press. These (which, of course, reflect EC regulations) may be summarised as follows:

For vehicles first used on or after 1 August 1983, a maximum of 4.5% carbon monoxide. For vehicles first used between 1 August 1975 and 31 July 1983, a maximum of 6% carbon monoxide. For vehicles first used on or after 1 August 1975, a maximum of 1200ppm (parts per million) hydrocarbons.

Any carburettor adjustment other than for 'fast idle', something we'll come to later, must be made only when the engine has attained normal running temperature. Similarly, the MoT tests must only be applied to a warmed-up engine.

50B

For all this talk of 'emissions', then, it can be realised that essentially it's still all down to the basic 'idle' and 'mixture' carburettor adjustments with which DIY motorists have been tinkering since time immemorial!

The idle adjustment alters the engine speed, the mixture adjustment alters (usually) the ratio of fuel to air: adding more fuel to the air enriches the mixture, cutting down on the fuel weakens the mixture.

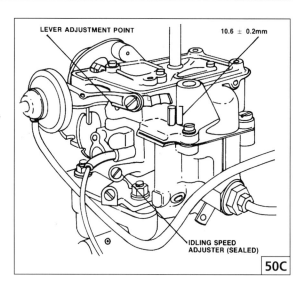

50C. As we said earlier in this section, we can only generalise, and generally the idle (or tick-over) adjuster on a basic 'fixed-jet' carburettor will be a screw near the bottom of the carburettor, threaded through a lug or bracket and bearing on the throttle spindle linkage - screwing it in or out will have the effect of rotating the spindle (and thus the 'butterfly' valve within the carb) either more open (fast) or more closed (slow). Sometimes (as would normally be the case with the GM Varajet example illustrated) even the idle adjustment will be sealed.

50D. The mixture adjuster, also a screw, may be in the same general locality, but actually set into the carburettor body, as on this Solex. This mixture screw, again generally speaking, will also be known as a 'volume control' screw, where unscrewing it (anticlockwise) increases the fuel flow through the carb's idle circuit, thus enriching the mixture; turning it clockwise cuts down the amount of fuel, thus weakening the mixture.

50E. A quite individual example is Ford's VV carburettor.

A variation found on some older fixed-jet carbs is that the mixture screw is, in fact, an 'airscrew'. Probably mounted higher up than a volume control screw, the airscrew (as its name implies) varies the amount of air (rather than the fuel) in the mixture, so unscrewing it weakens the mixture, and screwing it in enriches it.

Sometimes there will be a 'by-pass' screw, usually larger and fitted just above the mixture screw: the 'by-pass' screw regulates the flow of fuel/air for idling and is used, rather than mechanical adjustment, to set the idle speed.

Less common than fixed-jet (although often synonymous with 'performance' and frequently mounted in pairs) are the 'variable-jet' (or 'variable-choke, or 'constant-depression') carburettors as typified by the SU and Stromberg. Here the idle adjustment will be of much the same mechanical disposition as for the fixed-jet units, but the mixture adjustment will usually differ.

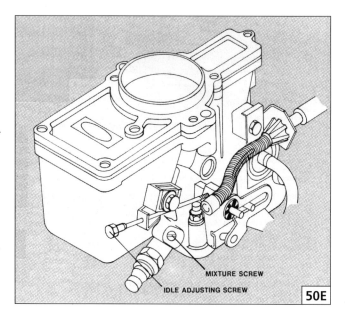

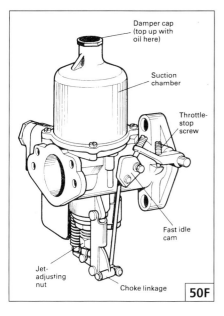

Damper cap
(top up with
oil here)

Suction
chamber

Throttle-
stop
screw

Fast idle
cam

Jet-
adjusting
nut

Choke linkage

50F

50F. On early 'H' and 'HS' SUs, the hexagonal jet adjusting nut, found centrally beneath the carburettor, is unscrewed (anti-clockwise, as viewed from below) to draw the jet downwards and thus enrich the mixture, or is screwed up (clockwise) to raise the jet and weaken the mixture.

50G. The later 'HIF' SUs have a conventional-looking mixture (jet adjusting) screw set into the body of the carb which is turned clockwise to enrich the mixture, and vice versa.

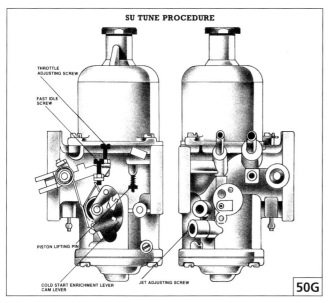

SU TUNE PROCEDURE

THROTTLE
ADJUSTING SCREW

FAST IDLE
SCREW

PISTON LIFTING PIN

COLD START ENRICHMENT LEVER
CAM LEVER

JET ADJUSTING SCREW

50G

50H. Early Stromberg mixture adjustment is similar to early SU, while on later models it is the needle height which is adjusted, using a special tool (available from accessory shops) inserted through the damper orifice: turning it clockwise screws the needle down and weakens the mixture, turning it anti-clockwise raises the needle and enriches the mixture. Later still only an 'idle trimming' screw is fitted, offering very limited mixture adjustment, clockwise to enrich, anti-clockwise to weaken.

INSIDE INFORMATION: You might like to note that, again generally speaking, on a fixed-jet carburettor these adjustments will affect the mixture over a very limited rev range, little more than from idling speed to just above, when the main jet(s) take over from the idling circuit, whereas the adjustment will probably affect most of the rev range on variable-jet carburettors.

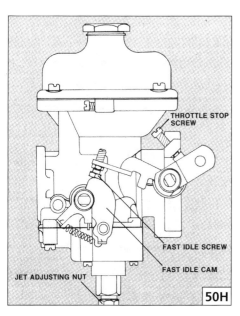

THROTTLE STOP
SCREW

FAST IDLE SCREW

FAST IDLE CAM

JET ADJUSTING NUT

50H

Once you know where the adjusters are, and have the tool to fit, the adjustment procedure is very simple. Where possible the air cleaner(s) should be left in place, since they do have some effect on the intake of air, and it is vital that the filter elements are clean - see '12,000-mile service' later.

On a fixed-jet carburettor, a typical procedure would be as follows:

i. Have the engine at normal running temperature, as previously mentioned. If it has been idling for a while already, and whenever it does so for an appreciable time between adjustments, 'blip' the throttle (to 'clear the throat'!) and pause until the idle settles down again.

ii. Adjust the idle screw to give a slightly faster idle than normal.

iii. Adjust the mixture screw in or out until the engine either begins to 'hunt' or suffer from an irregular 'lumpy' idle: 'hunting' is typified by a rhythmical rise and fall in engine speed, and results from an over-weak mixture; 'lumpy' running indicates an over-rich mixture.

iv. Now adjust the mixture screw between these two extremes to achieve the fastest, smoothest engine speed, preferably erring on the 'weak' side.

v. Re-set the idle screw to give the correct idle speed, returning to the mixture screw for fine adjustment if needs be to balance correct idle with smooth running.

50I. You could call this 'tuning by ear', but if you do have a CO meter (gas analyser) the procedure will remain the same except that you 'tweak' the screws, again concentrating on the mixture but still balancing one against the other, until you get the required reading on the CO scale - precise instructions for using the meter would, of course, come with the unit, this one the more sophisticated version referred to earlier.

50I

It has to be said that it does much for one's peace of mind to be sure that not only have you tuned the carb correctly, but that also you are 'legal'!

The same adjustment criteria apply to the variable-jet carbs, the only variation being that instead of screwing a mixture adjuster in or out you screw a jet adjuster, or a needle adjuster, up or down. However, looking in particular at the more prevalent SU, there may be some initial work required before making any tuning adjustment - this we will come to shortly.

With all adjustments, it is important to move the adjuster only a fraction at a time, waiting for around ten seconds each time for the adjustment to take effect before adjusting further.

Should you suspect that the present state of tune is way off what it should be, and particularly where previous service history is unknown, you may prefer to start from a 'datum' point, which entails setting the mixture adjustment (engine switched off) to a position which shouldn't be too far removed from a reasonable state of tune.

This can generally be achieved on a fixed-jet carb by gently screwing the adjuster fully in (never tighten it, or you'll almost certainly damage it) and then by unscrewing it one-and-a-half turns.

On the variable-jet SU, the jet adjusting nut should be turned clockwise to raise the jet until it is flush, or as nearly so as possible, with its bridge (the bit that the piston rests on) and the nut then unscrewed two complete turns (12 flats). However, since it may be difficult to verify whether the jet is flush with the bridge without partially dismantling the carb, it would be convenient here to describe the pre-tune work which is sometimes necessary, as mentioned earlier.

Basically, you need to ensure that the carburettor piston can rise and fall freely: over lengthy service or through previous neglect, dirt may build up on the carb internal surfaces, causing the piston action to be sticky.

Looking at the mouth of the carburettor (air cleaner removed) if you feel to the left or right of the body, just behind the air cleaner mounting flange, you may discover a spring-loaded pin (the 'piston lifting pin') which was fitted to many SUs. Pressing this pin upwards should lift the piston clear of the jet bridge. If there is no pin, lift the piston with your finger or a screwdriver blade - with either method, when you let go the piston should fall freely and contact the bridge with an audible 'click'.

If the action is sluggish, hopefully a clean-up is all that is required, although there are other possible causes (bent needle or off-centre jet, for example) which would call for more specialist attention.

For cleaning (or for better visual verification that the jet is flush with the bridge) the suction chamber (dashpot) must be removed. Before removing the securing screws, use something like a felt-tip pen to mark dashpot and carb body so the dashpot may be replaced in its original position.

50J

50J. When you lift away the pot and piston, have rag handy to catch oil escaping from the damper and retain the piston spring for re-fitment in its original position. Note that the piston has a keyway, and can only be replaced in its original position.

Use either a proprietary carb cleaner, or Castrol's aerosol 'DWF' is handy, and clean, lint-free rag to ensure the dashpot's internal surfaces and piston exterior are spotlessly clean - do not use an abrasive cleaner. It is not a bad idea to clean the whole of the carb exterior (but don't lose your alignment marks!) while you're at it, using a brush to dislodge heavy deposits, but be very careful not to transfer dirt into the carb interior.

50K.

50K. Now check, by adjusting as described earlier, that the top of the jet is flush with the bridge.

When you have reassembled the parts, having checked that jet position, hopefully you'll find now that the piston falls freely, with a 'click' as it meets the bridge. Don't forget to top up the dampers with clean oil.

Returning to the adjustments (on a warmed-up engine, of course) there is another, primary, use for that piston lifting pin - or you can use a screwdriver, lifting the piston approximately 1/32 in. (0.8 mm). As you gently lift, if the mixture is correct there should be a slight and short increase in engine rpm: a rich mixture would cause a considerable and sustained increase, while a weak mixture would result in a marked and immediate decrease, possibly stalling the engine.

If you have a multiple carb installation, the situation becomes decidedly more complex!

Typically, we would be looking at twin SUs or Strombergs. The problem is that not only must each carb be properly tuned, but that their individual states of tune must be balanced one with the other. It becomes more difficult when one carb is more worn than the other, which is often the case, the front or 'leading' carb usually attracting more abrasive dirt (and resultant spindle wear) than the rear carb.

It could be argued that we're moving into the realms of specialist tuning, but a basic procedure (having initially warmed-up the engine) is as follows:

i.   Remove the air cleaners.

ii. Slacken the two clamp bolts on the throttle spindle operating arms, and the two clamp bolts on the choke spindle operating arms.

iii. Unscrew the idle adjusters until the throttles just close, then open the throttles by screwing down each adjuster one complete turn.

iv. Start the engine (without using the throttle pedal) and let it idle.

50L.

50L. The Gunson 'Carbalancer' seen in action here is an example of the tuning aid mentioned earlier.

v.   Preferably use a proprietary carb balancing device available from accessory shops. Otherwise, use a short length of such as heater hose, one end to your ear, the other to the mouth of the carb, to listen to the air intake 'hiss' at each carb: turn the idle adjustment screws (a fraction at a time) until the intensity of the 'hiss' is the same on both carbs - the proprietary tuning aid would register when the air intake is the same for both carbs.

vi. Set the idling speed to that recommended for the car by turning each adjuster an equal amount.

vii. Re-tighten the clamp bolts on the throttle spindle operating arms, ensuring there is a slight clearance between the peg and the lower edge of the fork, and that both throttles open at the same time when the accelerator (throttle) pedal is depressed.

viii. Now adjust the mixture on each carburettor as described previously, turning each adjuster by the same amount and keeping the jets pressed upwards as you turn the nuts.

ix. Re-set the idle speed as necessary, again turning each adjuster an equal amount.

x.   Re-tighten the choke spindle clamps, using the same procedure as for the throttle connections.

Finally, we come to the 'fast-idle' adjustment that we mentioned early on in this section. Basically, this is a mechanism (usually adjustable) between the choke and throttle linkage that opens the throttle slightly when the choke is operated - we're presuming 'manual', rather than 'automatic' choke.

50M.

50M. The real value of this mechanism is in allowing initial movement of the choke control to open the throttle slightly before actual operation of the choke. It comes into its own when, after a cold-start, the engine will no longer run happily on choke, but is not yet warm enough to idle without danger of stalling - pushing the choke control far enough in to close the choke should still retain a slightly open throttle, i.e., a 'fast idle'.

50N. Very often, as on the SUs we have just been looking at, there will be a screw-and-lock-nut adjuster bearing on a cam (see also 50F and 50G). Sometimes your handbook will give a feeler gauge measurement to be set between the screw and cam. Typically, having first checked that the jets close up fully against their adjusting nuts when the choke control is pushed in, the adjustment (on a warm engine) should be such that when the choke is pulled out as far as it will go without moving the jets the fast idle is around 1000rpm. Sometimes a cold-engine fast-idle speed will also be specified.

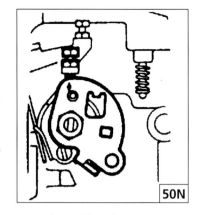

Fixed-jet carburettors may feature similar screw-and-cam fast-idle adjustment (with engine speed or gap measurement specified) or there may simply be a tab bearing on the cam - careful bending of the tab will adjust the fast idle. You can remove the air cleaner and watch the choke flap movement, adjusting for a comfortable fast idle before the choke flap starts to operate.

It may take trial and error to find a fast idle that best suits your requirements, but it can make a tremendous difference (even a safety contribution) to smooth, positive engine performance in cold-start, cold-weather conditions.

☐ **Job 51. Check clutch adjustment.**

This is a job that should only apply to older cars, since manual clutch adjustment is rarely provided for on modern cars - there may well be built-in automatic adjustment on modern cable linkage systems, while a hydraulic system is largely self-adjusting.

51A. You should also lubricate the clutch cable at this stage, as shown. Strictly speaking, it is not the clutch itself which is adjusted, but rather it is the elimination of unwanted free play in the clutch linkage: wear and tear here (talking mainly older cars) can reach the point where full clutch pedal movement barely releases the clutch - a fact underlined by difficult and noisy gearchanges.

Note, however, that generally a specified clutch adjustment would maintain measurable 'free play'. If there were no free play, then there was certainly the danger that the carbon facing of the old type clutch release bearing (the bit, fitted to the internal end of the clutch release lever, that actually presses against the clutch to release it) would grind away prematurely: that would mean an engine or gearbox removal operation just to renew that one small component. There was also some danger that the car would be driven with the clutch partially released, causing the clutch friction plate to slip and, again, grind away prematurely.

The ball-race release bearing that succeeded the carbon type is far longer lasting. And, indeed, sometimes an adjustment specified in the car handbook (perhaps that the clutch and brake pedals should be level, or that the clutch pedal should be a certain distance from floor or steering wheel) would ensure that the bearing was in 'constant contact' with the clutch.

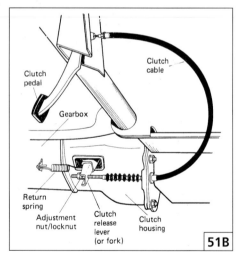

Obviously, the handbook for your car will tell you whether your clutch is adjustable, and if so what the adjustment should be.

51B. Typically, on an elderly rear-wheel drive car there will be an adjuster where the linkage from the pedal meets the clutch release lever (or 'fork') at the gearbox clutch housing (or 'bell-housing'). There will be a threaded section with a nut and lock-nut. And possibly the specification will be that, with the release lever (return spring temporarily removed) pulled away from the nuts until the release bearing is felt to contact the clutch, there should then be, perhaps, an inch gap between the lever and nuts: if not, then the nuts should be 'unlocked' and screwed along to obtain the correct gap - the specified 'free play'.

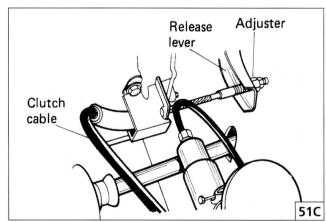

51C. Sometimes a similar linkage and adjuster would be found on the transmission housing under the bonnet of early front-wheel drive cars.

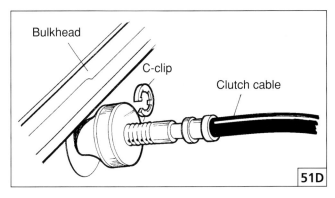

Bulkhead

C-clip

Clutch cable

51D

51D. Sometimes, instead, some sort of adjuster will be found where the clutch release cable passes through the engine compartment bulkhead. Here, rather than a threaded adjuster, there could be simply a C-clip in a choice of grooves - typically it might be specified that there should be five or six grooves between the clip and its abutment point when the outer cable is pulled away from the bulkhead.

There were some older hydraulic-clutch cars that also had a threaded adjustment on the pushrod between the clutch slave cylinder and the clutch release lever. Generally, though, no adjustment is fitted (or required) on a hydraulic set-up - but there has been a notable exception.

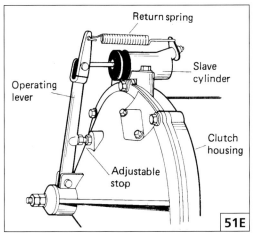

Return spring

Slave cylinder

Operating lever

Clutch housing

Adjustable stop

51E

51E. The venerable Mini, and the Metro, 'till the mid-eighties, incorporated adjustment in their hydraulic clutch linkage. In fact, until Jan '82 there were two adjustment points. Normally, only one would require regular attention - the adjustable stop found at a point roughly half-way up the release lever, basically a bolt and locknut fitted into the clutch housing and an abutment on the release lever. To check the adjustment, the return spring fitted between the release lever and a bracket on the clutch hydraulic slave cylinder should first be removed. Then pull the release lever away from the engine, until all free play is taken up, and use feeler gauges to measure the gap now opened up between the lever abutment and adjustable stop: the specification has varied over the years, but generally it should be 0.060 in. on early (pre-'69) Minis, 0.020 in. on later models, and 0.040 in. on the early Metro. If necessary, slacken the locknut and screw the bolt in or out to achieve the correct adjustment. Don't forget to re-fit the return spring.

The other adjustment, to the clutch plunger 'throw-out stop', should only be necessary immediately after a new clutch has been fitted. However, if your car's previous history is uncertain, and particularly if you are experiencing difficult gearchanges, you might like to check it out.

51F

51F. The plunger is the bit that the release lever pushes in and out, and at its inner end is the clutch release bearing. At its outer end, screwed up against the boss on the clutch housing, is the throw-out stop and its locknut (arrowed) - you can see it in this picture, just above the engine mounting, and also in 51E.

On the Mini and Metro to Jan '82, it should be set up as follows: slacken the locknut and unscrew the stop and locknut to the limit of the plunger thread; ask an assistant to hold the clutch pedal fully depressed while you now screw the stop and locknut back along the plunger until the stop contacts the boss on the clutch housing; with the clutch pedal then released, screw in the stop one further spanner flat and secure it in this position with the locknut; re-check the adjustable stop setting.

From Jan '82 a different design of clutch was fitted, the adjustable stop was deleted and the throw-out stop setting is slightly different: unscrew the stop and locknut to the end of the thread; pull the release lever away from the clutch housing, by hand, until you feel the release bearing contact the clutch; hold the lever in this position and screw the stop back in until a clearance of 0.26 in. (6.5 mm) exists between the stop and the boss on the clutch housing; hold the stop steady and tighten the locknut.

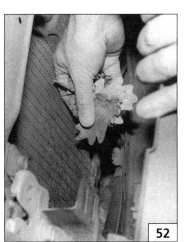

52

☐ Job 52. Cooling system.

Check the cooling and systems for leaks and all hoses for condition and tightness. Look at the ends of hoses for leaks - check clamps for tightness, if necessary and pinch the hoses to ensure that they are not starting to crack and deteriorate. If you don't want a hose to burst and let you down in the worst possible place, change any hose that seems at all suspicious.

Not all hoses are easily seen. For instance, the Mini heater hoses go through the bulkhead and make their connection inside the car, so don't overlook these check-points or you could have scalding water squirting over your ankles. (See also Job 72 and 92)

52. It is also worth checking to ensure that an accumulation of autumnal leaves is not restricting the air flow through the radiator.

☐ Job 53. Coolant check.

Use an anti-freeze hydrometer (available quite cheaply from accessory shops) to check the specific gravity (anti-freeze content) of the coolant. The tester will probably show a reading using coloured balls. If the concentration is below the recommended amount, top up the system with anti-freeze until the correct specific gravity is obtained. Of course the engine will have to be run for the newly introduced anti-freeze to mix thoroughly otherwise a false reading will be had. If you have any doubt over the period that the old mix has been in the car, drain and refill with fresh. (See also 'Anti-freeze', Job 73.)

54A

INSIDE INFORMATION Some owners think that there is little to be gained by using anti-freeze all the year round, particularly in those parts of the world where frost is not a problem. Wrong! Anti-freeze even in the minimum concentration of 25% not only gives protection against around -13 degrees Celsius (9 degrees Fahrenheit) or frost, it also contains corrosion inhibitors to stop the radiator from clogging and so helps to keep the car running cooler.

☐ Job 54. Heater controls.

54A. Check that all heater controls (and water valves) work smoothly and effectively. Some valves are prone to leaks or seizure. Treat with releasing fluid if seized, with thin oil if working. Ditto the control cable, adding oil or fluid to the ends before working the heater control open and shut a good few times.

54B

54B. Particularly prone to problems are the water control valves mounted on the engine of the Mini and other cars using the Rover 'A' series engines.

☐ Job 55. Check water pump.

SAFETY FIRST!
Ensure the engine is turned off and the battery disconnected.

55. Check the water pump for leaks - the first sign of mechanical failure - by looking for water leaks or stains around the spindle. So hidden are many pumps, that it will be almost impossible to do this visually, so the best you can do is to feel around the pump and check your hands for water or try rocking the cooling fan, if it's of the mechanical type. **SPECIALIST SERVICE** - Any problems should be dealt with by your specialist if much has to be dismantled to get access to the pump.

55

☐ Job 56. Check automatic transmission fluid.

The automatic transmission fluid ('ATF') is normally checked after a run, when the fluid will have reached normal operating temperature, with the engine idling and the gear selector lever in 'Park' ('P').

56A. Look for a dipstick similar to that for the engine oil. But on a rear-wheel drive car it would be set in a long tube disappearing backwards from the engine, towards the transmission unit behind the engine, while on a front-wheel drive car it should be mounted actually on the transmission unit in the engine compartment. A typical procedure might be to set the handbrake then, with the engine idling, hold the brake pedal down while you shift the selector lever from 'P' through each gear range, and then back to 'P'.

56A

With the engine still idling, withdraw the dipstick and wipe it clean. Examine the marks on the bottom end - there may be just maximum and minimum level marks, like the engine oil dipstick, or these may be duplicated and marked 'cool' and 'hot'. The 'cool' check (engine hasn't been run for about five hours) would give a reasonable indication of the fluid level; make an accurate 'hot' check as soon as possible.

56B. Re-insert the stick, withdraw it again, and check where the wet fluid line registers - if it falls markedly short of the maximum mark, the recommended brand of ATF should be added to bring the level up: usually, the fluid has to be added, using a funnel, into the dipstick tube, which, given the narrow bore of the tube, can be a tricky operation!

Whether just checking the level or adding fluid, it is essential to maintain absolute cleanliness, since any dirt entering the system can seriously affect its operation.

Job 57. Check power steering fluid.

If your car has power assisted steering, it will almost certainly have an oil reservoir remote from the steering rack or box, maybe remote also from the belt-driven pump unit.

57A. Unscrewing the lid (first clean away any surface dirt) should bring with it an integral dipstick, marked with maximum and minimum levels. Sometimes the reservoir may be translucent, with the levels marked on its exterior.

Note that these level marks may be duplicated for 'Hot' or 'Cold' conditions: the former might apply if, for instance, the car has just been driven for 20 minutes or so at around 50mph, the latter if the engine has not been run for about five hours. Beware of burns if you are making a 'Hot' check.

Top-up as necessary, using the oil specified in your handbook - generally automatic transmission fluid ('ATF').

57B. Incidentally, while a steering box (rather than today's steering rack) is rarely found these days, except on larger cars, where it will almost certainly be power assisted, there are still older cars around that will have one fitted. And vehicles such as motor caravans based on older-design commercial chassis may also feature a box - e.g., the older, but still prolific, VW 'bus'.

The box (look for it literally at the end of the steering column) is generally filled with SAE 90 oil, and this should last for ever unless leakage occurs. It is still a good idea to remove the filler plug at regular intervals to check that the oil level is up to the bottom of the plug hole.

Around the Car

Job 58. Check seat belts.

Make sure the seat belts are clean and not showing signs of fraying or other damage.

58. Make sure that if you pull slowly, the belt unreels smoothly; but also make sure that if you pull sharply that the belt immediately locks up.

Check that the buckles latch securely.

Check that the reel mounting is secure.

☐ **Job 59. Renew wiper blades.**

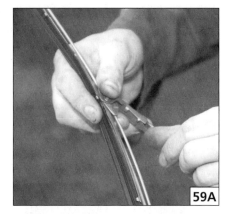

Here is a job that is time related, rather than mileage related. Wiper blades should certainly be given a look-over every week or so (refer back to Job 14) but should then be given a really thorough check every six months, rather than the once a year at best (probably MoT time) that is too often the case.

And given how dangerous it can be on the roads today if your windscreen cannot be kept crystal clear in foul weather conditions, there may even be grounds for supporting the wiper blade manufacturers' recommendation that the blades should actually be renewed every six months.

59A. Anyway, a conscious appraisal of wiper performance at six-monthly intervals, plus visual inspection of the blade rubber, may well remind you that of late the blades have become more inclined to smear, streak or judder, rather than quietly sweep the screen clean, and that indeed the rubber feels hard and looks ragged.

A good accessory shop will be able to advise you as to whether you need complete replacement blades, or whether new rubber 'refills' can be fitted to your existing blades - diagrammatic fitting instructions will come with the pack.

59B. You will need to know the length of your wiper blades, and it is advisable to measure both driver's and passenger's side, since sometimes they are of unequal length. Don't forget, also, to check the rear wiper, where fitted.

59C. Should a wiper arm need to be removed (perhaps for re-positioning on its splines to obtain a better sweep of the screen), some can just be pulled or levered off, perhaps after removing a locking screw, or lifting the arm to relieve spring tension, while others...

59D. ...will be secured by a nut, having first pulled off its protective cover.

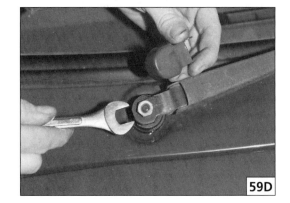

Job 60. Locks and hinges.

OIL CAN LUBE

It doesn't always figure highly, if at all, in service schedules, but there are a fair few moving parts on the motor car which would benefit from occasional oil-can lubrication. They will then work more smoothly, probably more quietly, and will certainly last longer. Here are just a few examples - we have already touched on some earlier in the text, but if you get into the habit of regularly 'carrying the can' around your car, you'll probably spot a few more!

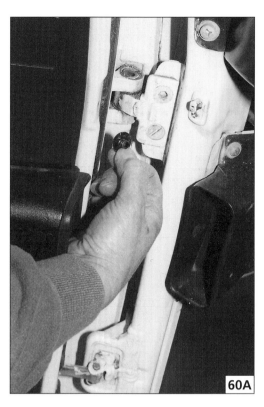

60A. Prime areas for neglect are the door hinges. On this well thought out design (actually on an elderly VW motor caravan!)...

60B. ...you first prise out a plastic cap from the top of the hinge, then direct the oil can nozzle into the hollow beneath.

60C. Actually a can of grease, rather than oil, but here a door check strap which, if left unlubricated, dries out, rusts up, and not only retards smooth door opening and closing, but also causes those strident 'graunching' noises which are always an embarrassment - particularly in your drive-way late at night! An occasional smear of grease works wonders.

60D. Another variation on the type of can: on older, or previously neglected door hinges, it could be beneficial to first douse them with penetrating fluid, following up with the oil can a little later, when the penetrating stuff has done its work.

60E. The penetrating fluid, using the can's slim 'accessory tube', is handy for penetrating key lock mechanisms, or door lock push-buttons.

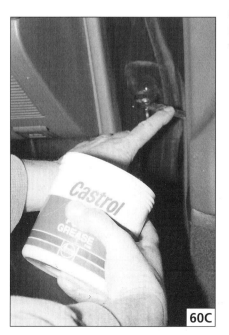

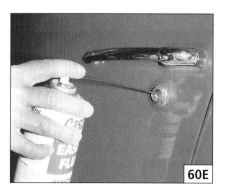

60F. Don't forget the door latch mechanisms, too, for, as with the hinges, lack of lubrication here soon leads to wear and noise, and the door drops out of alignment and has to be slammed shut - more noise, more wear!

☐ **Job 61. Cable mechanisms.**

61A. While you've got the oil can or tin of grease to hand, go back under the bonnet. If the bonnet latch is not kept lubricated one day you may find you can't, in fact, get under the bonnet, because the latch has rusted and seized. There are possible 'emergencies' that could arise from this, but even more horrific is when a bonnet that has not closed securely flies open when you are driving! Lubricate the bonnet release and safety catch using clean silicone grease so that you won't soil clothes when leaning into the engine bay. Lubricate the bonnet hinges too.

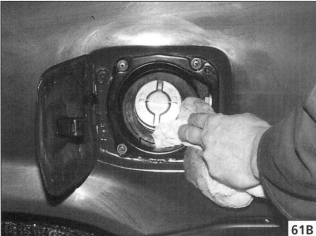

61B. Also lubricate the boot or tailgate lock, and petrol filler flap latch and hinges. If they have a remote release inside the car, lubricate the release cable - if you can get at it! But note that many remote releases are electrically operated, in which case, DON'T APPLY OIL! A case in point is a remote operated petrol filler flap, but at least lubricate the flap hinge and catch, and keep the area clean.

IMPORTANT NOTE: Do not lubricate the steering lock, except with a drop of oil on the end of a key to prevent the lock barrel from seizing.

61C. There could be quite a bit of external linkage around the carburettor which would benefit from the occasional drop of oil, and help to make the car sweeter to drive.

61D. A stretch of rusting heater control cable caught the eye here, but as we said, keep looking and you may well find a number of other linkages or mechanisms which will be the better for regular oil-can maintenance.

☐ Job 62. Check seats.

62A. Check the condition and security of all seats. The front ones should slide smoothly (for adjustment) and latch securely as well as being securely mounted, while...

62B. ...the rear ones (with very few exceptions) may not slide but obviously must be securely mounted. Sliding mechanisms should be kept clean and occasionally lubricated with a smear of silicone grease.

☐ Job 63. Test dampers.

Bounce each corner of the car in turn in order to check the efficiency of the shock absorbers. If the car 'bounces' at all, the shock absorbers have had it. They should be replaced in pairs and efficient shock absorbers can make an enormous difference to your car's safety and handling.

☐ Job 64. Check/renew disc brake pads.

As well as the 'low fluid' warning light we mentioned earlier, when talking of topping-up the brakes hydraulic fluid reservoir, some brake systems have an electrical sensor built into the disc pad mounting that will illuminate another warning light on the fascia, to alert the driver to the fact that the pad friction material has worn to the point where it would be prudent to renew the pads.

(Sometimes one warning light serves several possible brake system malfunctions, plus reminding you that the handbrake is applied).

A somewhat cruder system also exists, whereby the reducing friction material thickness will eventually allow a metal clip on the pads to touch the brake disc, causing a warning squeal.

Where no pad wear warning system exists, the car handbook should at least specify a minimum permissible friction material thickness and will normally recommend that the pads are inspected every 6000 miles.

Minimum pad thickness recommendations may vary from, say, 1/16 in. (1.5 mm) to double this, 1/8 in. (3 mm). It is wiser to work to the higher figure, since it can be a relatively short step from 1/16 in. to the 'warning squeal' that tells you that a pad metal backing plate is now rubbing on the disc! Not only will the brakes be dangerously ineffective, but also expensive disc damage will be taking place.

On older cars, where the disc brake unit is fairly well exposed, you might be able to see the pads quite clearly. On more modern cars, with deeply dished road wheels, the brake unit may be almost totally enclosed by the wheel.

64A. Sometimes the cut-outs of the wheel design allow viewing of the pads through a 'window' let into the brake calliper - although you may need to first remove any wheel trim and you may also need a pencil-beam torch for a clear view.

Often, even for just checking, you will need to remove the road wheel. And even then the pads may still be visible only through a window as just described, with maybe the torch still required as well.

Remember it is the friction material thickness you are checking, not the total pad thickness. (That said, some manufacturers have been known to give a total friction material/backing plate thickness - e.g., 7mm).

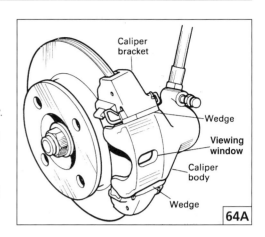

If the pads need renewing, some dismantling is called for, varying from easy to slightly tricky, according to the calliper design.

(The pads must also be renewed in 'axle sets' - i.e., new pads on both offside and nearside wheels of the same axle).

64B. Probably the easiest to deal with are the older fixed calliper designs. Here the calliper is bolted rigidly to the hub unit, with each half of the calliper containing one or more pistons operating each pad individually. Generally, the pads will be secured by two long pins passing through both calliper and pad backing plates: these pins may be entirely self-securing or they may be additionally secured by split-pins or 'hairgrip' type pins passed through holes in their ends, or they may themselves be of split-pin design. The pins may also secure a spring clip or plate against the edges of the pads.

The important thing is to note how any such clip or plate is positioned, which way round any pin is fitted and from which side of the calliper it should be withdrawn (or, carefully, punched out) and into which side it should be inserted first when re-fitting - write it down or sketch it.

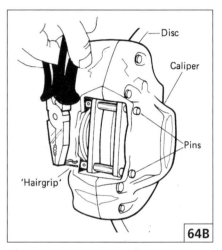

With the securing pins out, and any spring clip or plate removed, there is now a fairly large area in the back of the calliper through which the old pads can be withdrawn. Be warned, however, that they can be inclined to jam, particularly where there is much accumulation of brake dust. Gripping with pliers and pulling alternately top and bottom, or even using a slim drift at the other end, may work, but by far the easiest solution, before even starting the job, is to equip yourself with a brake pad pulling tool, a sort of 'slide hammer' that pegs into the pad securing pin holes.

(Although many brake pads these days will be of 'non-asbestos' formulation, you cannot be sure what has been fitted to your vehicle previously, so do not on any account risk breathing in any of that brake dust just referred to, since it could be highly injurious to your health. Either carefully vacuum it away, or use a damp cloth to collect it).

64C. As you withdraw the pads, take note of any difference in pattern from side to side, and watch out for the almost certain fitment of a shim to each pad backing plate: the shim might be metal, it might be semi-stuck to the backing plate with grease, it might be plastic, and it might even be literally stuck to the plate, although not rigidly. Whatever the case, the shims need to be retained for fitment to the replacement pads and note must be made of which way round they were originally fitted - they may, for instance, have raised portions that mate with cut-aways on the calliper pistons.

(Generally, these shims act as anti-squeal or anti-rattle devices).

On a swinging, floating, or sliding calliper design, the procedure will usually be slightly different. Here the pads are normally retained in a carrier bolted rigidly to the hub unit, while the calliper is free to swing (pivot), float or slide.

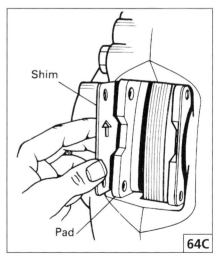

Only one side of the calliper will contain a piston, and the principle of operation is probably easier to understand with the (more prevalent, anyway) sliding design: as the brake pedal is depressed, the piston moves outwards to bear against the brake pad on its side, pushing the pad against the disc; as it meets firm resistance, and can no longer move outwards, the continuing fluid pressure now pushes the calliper away from the piston - as the calliper 'slides' on its guide pins, away from the piston, it pulls the pad on the opposite side also into firm contact with the disc.

(Where the calliper pivots or floats, the chain reaction from the initial movement of the single piston is the same).

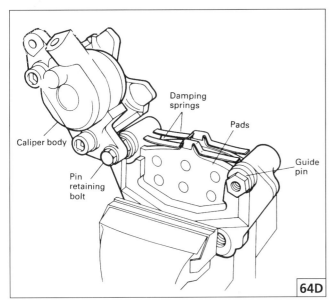

64D

Occasionally, the pad removal procedure for these moving calliper designs will be much the same as outlined for the fixed calliper unit, with the pads retained by pins or spring clips, or both, and sometimes a bolted plate and pin device. Again, make careful notes of what goes where, and how.

64D. Generally, however, the calliper will need to be unbolted and removed completely, or at least pivoted out of the way, to gain access to the pads - unfortunately we can't be specific as to which would be the case with your car, but possibly a friendly mechanic at your local dealer would tell you!. (In the drawing of our bench-mounted unit, one guide-pin bolt has been removed, and the calliper body pivoted clear of the pads).

64E. Anyway, on our typical sliding calliper design, look for two hexagon-headed or recess-headed guide pin bolts, one top and one bottom of the calliper unit. The recess-headed bolts may require an Allen key or a splined tool: typically, again, the Allen key required would be 7mm size and, as well as part of a set of such keys, these days it is often sold separately, with special high-leverage handle, specifically for this brake job (and also for the valve adjusters on some cars); many good-quality socket sets will also contain a selection of both Allen key and splined bits which can be used with a socket adaptor.

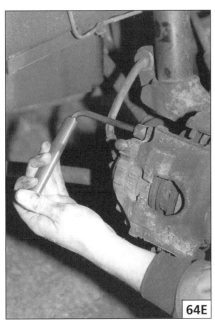

64E

Depending on the design, it might be possible, as we inferred earlier, to remove just one of these pin bolts (you might have to hold steady a locknut) and then pivot the calliper on the other pin (usually the top one, this often governed by the length of the flexible brake hose) until the pads are fully exposed. In some cases the other pin bolt may need to be slackened before the unit will pivot.

In other cases both pin bolts will have to be removed and the calliper unit then lifted out of the way. To be honest, even this is hardly a great chore and there are even hidden benefits, which we'll come to later. Meanwhile, having dismounted the calliper, make sure it is securely tied up out of the way, the important thing being to avoid putting undue strain on the flexible hydraulic hose.

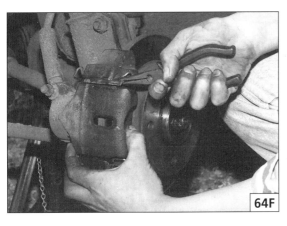

64F

A variation of the sliding calliper (as found, for instance, on older Ford Fiestas) has the calliper sliding on keyways; the calliper has to be dismounted for access to the pads:

64F. First remove the tiny split-pins that secure (top and bottom) the wedge-shaped calliper guides. The guides can then be pulled or carefully drifted out, the operation helped by depressing the calliper against its spring pressure.

With the guides removed, the calliper can be dismounted (you might need to depress one end and lift out the other) and tied up out of the way.

64G. In all cases, where the pads are now exposed, first note that in some instances there may be 'spreader' or anti-rattle springs pegged into the exposed edges of the pads, these springs needing to be detached and retained for fitment to the new pads; in other instances, variations of such springs may be permanently fixed to the pads, but do check your new pads have them fitted.

64H. The pads themselves should be easily lifted (perhaps prised with a screwdriver blade) from their housing: as you lift them, note how they peg into the housing, and watch out for anti-rattle and/or anti-squeal spring clips fitted to top or bottom edges of the pads - these may have to be transferred to the new pads, or the latter may come with them already fitted. Also look out for pad wear warning light electrical leads, which will have to be unplugged.

Again, watch out for pad backing shims and also for any difference in pad shape or pattern from one side to the other.

(In some instances, by the way, one pad will be housed in the dismounted calliper, in others a moving calliper left in situ will have to be levered sideways to release one of the pads).

64I. Again in all cases now, with the old pads removed, thoroughly clean up the pad housings and calliper bodies (particularly around the piston edges) and any retained parts, such as the shims. A toothbrush, rag, and either a specific brake cleaning fluid, methylated spirits, or something like Castrol's DWF will speed the work - but bear in mind our brake dust warning and heed any cautionary advice printed on the cleaning fluid.

Also clean the disc faces, ensuring they are entirely grease-free, and at the same time check that they are not unduly scored or so badly worn as to leave a prominent ridge around the disc circumference. A light ridge, perhaps mostly a build-up of rust, can be carefully removed with a file - on a fixed calliper set-up, it might be possible to feed the file (or a hefty old screwdriver) through a pad aperture, then steadying the file (or screwdriver blade) firmly against the ridge while you spin the disc.

64J. Badly scored or badly ridged discs will seriously reduce braking efficiency even with fully bedded-in pads. New pads would take for ever to bed-in on them and meanwhile braking efficiency could be virtually nil!

With luck, there might be enough 'meat' left on the discs for a local machine shop to grind them back to 'as new' condition. It will be cheaper to approach a machine shop direct (look in your local business directory) rather than take the discs to your local garage - the garage would probably still have to contract out the work to the machine shop, and then might add a handling charge or a percentage onto the machine shop bill!

Even if your discs are judged beyond redemption, shop around the High Street and other independent accessory and spares outlets for new - by all means ask your garage to quote a price, but, again, it will almost certainly cost you less elsewhere. (See also Job 93).

Anyway, with the brakes already at least partially dismantled, now is the time to tackle a duff disc. The fixed calliper would be unbolted from the hub assembly as a unit, leaving the disc clear, while on a moving calliper set-up the pad housing would probably need unbolting as well, before the disc could be lifted away from the hub.

64K. Again, we'll have to generalise, but you may find now that the disc is fully floating on the hub assembly (i.e., it is normally bolted to the hub by the road wheel bolts) or that a single screw or more hold it to the hub. However, I feel bound to warn you that (even when fully floating) in my experience the disc either literally falls off first go, or demands hours of penetrating oil and (careful) persuasion with such as a hefty copper hammer!

In extreme cases the hub has to be removed to the bench for more forceful treatment, perhaps even heating with a blowtorch.

So if your discs look both duff and determined, you might prefer to let someone else do the job!

Hopefully, there are no worries at all as far as your discs are concerned, so we can move on.

In order to make room for the new (obviously much thicker) disc pads, the calliper piston(s) must be pushed back into the cylinder bore(s) - one good reason why you have to be sure a piston's exposed circumference is absolutely clean, since it's vital that abrasive dirt doesn't get pushed back into the cylinder bore along with the piston.

64L. Here is the particular instance, inferred earlier, where there can be a hidden benefit in having to dismount a sliding calliper. It often requires a fair old push to get a piston back flush with the face of the calliper - but when it's dismounted, you have the room to employ something like the correct 'special tool' such as a large G-cramp...

64M. ...(or something like a valve spring compressor, should you happen to possess one') which will squeeze the piston back in relatively easily.

A fixed calliper is more of a problem, since here we're dealing with at least two pistons, and you will need to employ something like a large old screwdriver entered into the pad housings to lever the pistons back. The problems are compounded by the fact that the piston face is most likely 'hollowed', so you can only lever on the circumferential face on one side, this having the effect of tipping the piston sideways and possibly jamming it, and also there's a danger of the screwdriver blade slipping and scoring the side of the piston or damaging an exterior dust seal.

At the same time, any success in pushing the piston in on one side may also succeed in pushing the opposing piston further out, possibly right out!

(Of course, on something like a 'four pot' system, with two pistons on each side of the calliper, it gets even trickier!).

Fortunately, there is one simple answer to all these problems: clean up and temporarily re-insert the old pads - the leverage can now be applied between the disc and an old pad, this giving an even 'all round' push on the piston circumference (the same holding true for a pair of pistons on one side) and while you're levering in one pad aperture, the old pad the other side will contain the opposing piston(s). While it may be less vulnerable, obviously you must also be careful not to damage the disc face with your lever.

The procedure now, of course, is to fit a new pad (having pulled out the old) to the aperture where you have just levered back the piston(s) before moving to the next aperture to lever back the piston(s) there.

Should the old pads, by any chance, still be thick enough to make it difficult to get your lever in, it can readily be seen that the same idea will work by employing, perhaps, two pieces of hardwood of suitable size and thickness.

However, before squeezing, or levering any pistons back in, there is an under-bonnet precaution to take. Bear in mind that pushing pistons back in also pushes hydraulic fluid further back into the system, with the danger that the level in the master cylinder reservoir may rise to the point of overflow - messy, but also (as we've mentioned previously) this hydraulic fluid is both an excellent paint stripper and a possible fire risk.

You can use a 'dip-tube' to draw off some fluid from the reservoir. You will sometimes see manuals suggest opening a bleed-screw on the calliper to let fluid escape there, but we certainly regard this latter method as hazardous, inviting the twin evils of letting air into the brake system or (where it's old and perhaps corroded) possible breakage of the bleed-screw. Far simpler to just wrap rag around the reservoir to soak up any spillage.

64N. Before fitting a new pad, lightly smear the rear face of its backing plate and the faces of any shims (don't forget these!) with such as an assembly grease (usually copper-based) or a recognised anti-squeal grease - but be very careful not to get any on the friction material or disc face. Make sure, where necessary, that any clips on the old pads are transferred to the new, and don't forget, where appropriate, to refit any pad-wear sensor leads.

Before re-fitting, or swinging down a sliding calliper, make sure such items as spreader springs are pegged into the pad edges, or otherwise properly positioned - they are easily overlooked!

(Also use the copper-grease, or other recognised brake grease, on the keys and keyways of the Fiesta-type sliding calliper we mentioned).

INSIDE INFORMATION: On a fixed calliper, a slim electrical screwdriver can be useful for aligning pin-holes in calliper, shims and pad backing plates. Make sure all pins are fit for further service - where lightweight split-pins are used, these should be renewed as a matter of course. As you enter the main securing pins, don't forget here to also reposition any spring plates or clips previously fitted.

64N

When all is done, press the brake pedal several times to settle the pads and restore correct brake pedal travel - the initial lack of firmness can be disconcerting! Check the brake fluid level, topping-up as necessary.

Finally, remember that it takes time (maybe some hundreds of miles) for the new disc pads to bed-in and give maximum efficiency. (See also 24,000 mile 'reminder' in Job 94).

65A

☐ Job 65. Check drum brake.

Whereas disc brakes are generally self-adjusting, many drum brake installations, front and rear, will have provision for manual adjustment of the brake shoes to compensate for the friction lining wear which can lead to increased brake pedal travel and (potentially dangerous) unbalanced braking - see also the rest of this Job.

65A. Look for a squared protrusion on the drum backplate (arrowed): on front brakes there will normally be two such adjusters, diametrically opposed, one for each shoe; on rear brakes there will normally be just the one.

65B. A rare exception to the squared adjuster on rear brakes is a toothed wheel adjuster, normally accessible through a plugged aperture on the backplate, sometimes through an aperture in the drum face.

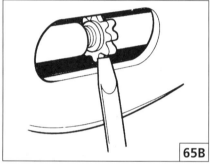

65B

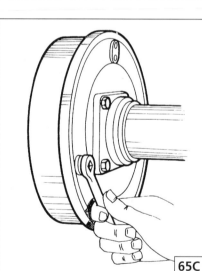

65C

65D

Often such an adjuster will have two toothed wheels, set close together, so each shoe is adjusted separately. The wheels can be turned by using a screwdriver blade, levering between the wheel teeth and the edge of the access aperture.

65C. After long service, the squared adjuster may be difficult to turn, and it's always advisable to buy a proper brake spanner for the job: this will be a sturdy item, whereas a 'make do' spanner is likely to slip and round off the adjuster.

65D. It is also advisable to give these adjusters a squirt of releasing fluid before attempting to turn them.

Looking at the brake backplate, generally squared adjusters should be turned clockwise to tighten the adjustment, anti-clockwise to slacken it. A twin toothed wheel adjuster normally requires the teeth on the right-hand wheel to be levered upwards to tighten its shoe, and vice versa on the left-hand adjuster wheel. Obviously, then, turning either the opposite way will slacken the adjustment.
Note that a single squared adjuster on a rear drum will generally have a tapered square section at its inner end which, as it screws in,

expands wedges to push the shoes nearer the drum. It is possible, during adjustment, to fetch up on a ridge of the inner squared section - to obviate this risk, always finish off by turning the adjuster slightly to and fro until you're sure it has 'settled' correctly.

To adjust, first slacken each adjuster until the wheel spins freely. Next, working on one adjuster at a time, turn it until the wheel locks up; now slacken off until the wheel just spins freely again - it is permissible for the shoes to be heard just rubbing slightly. After adjustment, operate the brake pedal and handbrake a few times to settle the shoes, then re-check the adjustment, altering it as necessary.

In the old days of 'drum brakes all round', it was a bit of a chore having to remove the brake drums on all four wheels in order to check the brake shoes. Then came the early examples of disc-front, drum-rear cars that are the norm today. With the early examples, checking the shoes had become less of a chore, with only the two rear drums to remove. But very soon the car manufacturers were able to boast of the easier (and, therefore, cheaper) maintenance offered by the provision of plugged 'peepholes' in their cars' brake drums - pull the plug (situated, usually, practically on the circumference of the drum backplate) and you could check the brake shoe lining thickness. Admittedly, it was only one shoe that you could see, but, generally, if that one was OK, then so was the other.

All very fine. Except that removing the drums also gave you the chance to make a check on other aspects of the brakes, maybe even more important than the thickness of the shoes - namely, whether there was any sign of brake fluid leakage from the wheel cylinder(s), or of (on live rear axle cars) oil leakage into the drums.

As with the pads, the average recommended minimum thickness for brake shoe linings is 1/16 in. (1.5 mm). Again, we suggest that that's too little, and that it would be safer to double the recommendation.

However, rear drum brake shoes (less highly stressed than front disc pads) will cover many thousands of miles before they need renewing, and will probably continue to work quite adequately down to that sixteenth of an inch - but a hydraulic fluid leak could leave you with a sudden serious loss of braking efficiency. And contamination of the linings, whether by hydraulic fluid or axle oil (or grease from an over-heated or otherwise faulty wheel-bearing) will certainly render the shoes inoperative, giving dangerously unbalanced braking.

Neither the wheel cylinder nor oil leakage, nor the lining contamination, is likely to be spotted through a hole that just gives an edge-on view of a short length of the shoe lining.

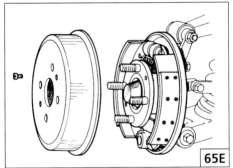

65E.

So it's best still to go to the bother of actually removing the drum? Good idea - except that along with the ease of lining thickness inspection offered by the plugs, sometimes comes increased difficulty of removing the drum!

Where the drum is still a separate item, there shouldn't be too much difficulty. It might be located on the hub assembly by one or more screws, counter-sunk or hexagon-headed, or there could be no screws at all, or maybe just a spring clip around one of the wheel studs. It is the road wheel that really locks it to the hub.

65E. Remove the wheel nuts, pull off the wheel, undo any screws or remove a clip, and the drum should shortly also be pulled off.

If there are exterior manual brake shoe adjusters, these will usually need first to be slackened off. Where automatic shoe adjustment is built-in there may be access holes in the drum face (maybe in the backplate) to insert, perhaps, two slim screwdriver blades, one to lift the actuating lever from a ratchet wheel, the other to turn the ratchet to slacken the shoes. If there's no access, then hopefully no de-adjustment is needed.

65F.

Sometimes an accumulation of rust around the hub boss or wheel stud holes will need dosing with penetrating oil. Sometimes an initial reluctance to move can be overcome by careful use of a copper hammer around the circumference (but not the lip) of the drum, striking it in an outwards direction - never lever between the drum and backplate.

It is where the brake drum and the wheel hub have been combined as one unit that removal can be more difficult. Of course, the hub nut must be undone, generally having first removed the grease, or dust cap, then a split-pin.

Where the cap has a rim on it, tapping such as a chisel blade between the rim and the nose of the hub, working evenly around the circumference, will usually force the cap outwards and off. In the rare event of there being no rim, a trick of the trade is to fasten a worm-drive clip around the cap and then lever or tap against the clip.

65F. Once access to the nut is gained (after the split-pin you may have to lift off a serrated nut retainer), if it's an adjustable (taper) bearing, the nut won't be very tight - your only worries now should be preventing the bearings dropping out of the hub into the dirt as you pull off the drum/hub and how to get the bearing adjustment right when you reassemble it all.

65G.

65G. Put clean rag on the ground to catch the bearings, and at least be sure on the outer bearing that you know which way round is fitted the (possibly bevelled) washer you'll find behind the nut. A taper bearing can only be fitted one way round, a typical adjustment procedure we'll come to later.

Still dealing with a combined drum/hub unit, where a non-adjustable (parallel) bearing is used, the hub nut might just be tight - or it might be exceedingly tight, like done up to close to 200lb/ft!

(Hub nuts on the nearside of the car may be left-hand thread, and obviously information on this and recommended tightening torques for a particular model will have to be sought by the owner).

If you decide to proceed, even though you won't have a torque wrench adjustable to such a high figure, you'll need a length of pipe sleeved over your socket bar to gain enough leverage to shift such a tight nut, and the trick is to take up the strain and then strike the pipe with a heavy hammer to shock the nut free. You'll need to be using at least a half-inch drive socket set, and make sure the socket is firmly on the nut - even then take every precaution to avoid slippage and possible damage to yourself or the car.

(It may help, by the way, to have an assistant sit in the car and apply the foot-brake firmly).

With the nut and washer (again, note which way round this fits) removed, the drum will usually pull off fairly easily. If it's reluctant, one advantage of the combined drum/hub unit is that you can temporarily replace the road wheel and use this to gain extra pulling power. In extreme cases you would have to hire a hub puller suitable for your car.

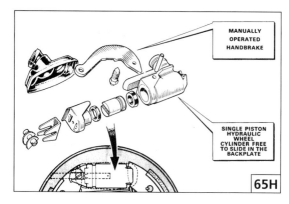

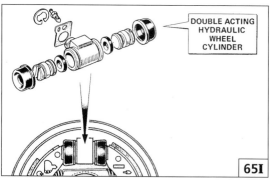

Having removed the drum, use a vacuum cleaner and/or damp cloth to remove brake dust from both the inside of the drum and the now exposed brake shoes and ancillary parts.

Obviously, you now have a much better view of brake shoe condition, but the main benefit of drum removal is to be able to inspect the hydraulic wheel cylinder(s), checking them for fluid leakage.

65H. Depending on the brake design, there may be just one, single-piston cylinder, mounted so that it can slide in the backplate, so that it operates both brake shoes in much the same way as does the single-piston sliding disc brake calliper.

65I. Or there may be two rigidly mounted, top and bottom, single-piston cylinders, or just one twin-piston (double acting) cylinder. Incidentally, whatever the design, they are sometimes referred to as 'slave cylinders'.

65J. Hopefully, no fluid leakage will anyway be immediately apparent, but you do need to carefully peel back the cylinder's rubber boot(s) to check that they are 'dry' inside. They might be greasy, but if they seem 'wet' dip your finger in and have a sniff - the smell of hydraulic fluid is pretty distinctive.

Hopefully, again, all will be well. But in this way the early stages of leakage can be detected in time both to avoid possible eventual brake failure and to protect the shoe linings from being ruined by fluid contamination. The same applies for early detection of axle oil leakage into the drum - here you'll spot the 'oiliness' building up on the brake backplate, behind the shoes.

For the moment, we'll now assume that everything can be reassembled. Obviously, much of it is a straightforward reversal of the original dismantling procedure, not forgetting to use new split-pins and maybe wiping away exuded old bearing grease and applying a liberal coating of fresh grease, which must be of the high-melting point (HMP) variety and suitable for the application check the wording on the can.

Where the hub nut was 'exceedingly tight', it's just possible you could do it up fairly tight and then drive to a friendly local garage (or possibly a tyre and exhaust centre) and pay a modest fee to have them tighten the nut to the correct torque. Otherwise, you'll just have to exercise common sense, and the length of pipe again, to tighten it as hard as you reasonably can.

On an adjustable (taper-roller) bearing set-up, there may be just a recommendation that the hub nut is tightened until, with the road wheel on, there is just perceptible 'play' when the wheel is rocked vertically by grasping it top and bottom.

65K. But sometimes a nut torque will be specified in your car data, and the bearing adjustment procedure could be typified by, for instance, that given for early Ford Fiestas. Here, a torque wrench should be used to first tighten the nut to 27lb/ft; then, while at the same time rotating the hub, the nut should be backed off 90 degrees.

You would probably find that, with the wheel back on, this would leave the just perceptible play referred to earlier. In all cases, though, after this reassembly adjustment, re-check the play after, say, 20 miles or so.

If, however, your checks did reveal that a new wheel cylinder must be fitted, or that the brake shoes must be replaced, it should be said that such work is really moving to the higher realms of DIY, and you might want to consider very carefully whether you want to tackle it. On the other hand, understandably, you might feel it would be a shame not being able to 'finish the job' having come thus far.

Unfortunately, here is another area where we can only generalise and hope that any typical procedure described would be sufficient to show what could be required on your car.

(With this sort of work, and maybe where you have to tackle wheel bearings, as mentioned earlier, you might consider enlisting the services of a trained mechanic, perhaps for only a modest fee, to either look over your shoulder while you work, or to vet it when you've finished).

Looking first at hydraulic wheel cylinder replacement, note that it may well be 'handed': when buying new you would have to specify whether it's a front or rear wheel, whether it's nearside or offside and whether (where appropriate) it's top or bottom - one may not be interchangeable with another.

Note, also, that inevitably when dismantling some fluid will be lost, and air will enter the system, which will mean the need to 'bleed' the air out of the system after the job is done. 'Bleeding' we'll explain later, but meanwhile the problem can be limited to some extent by restricting the amount of fluid lost.

65L. Probably the most effective way of doing this is to clamp a self-grip wrench over the nearest flexible brake hose to the cylinder you're replacing: the hose only needs 'nipping', don't murder it. Another 'trick' is to place a sheet of cellophane over the neck of the master cylinder reservoir and then screw the cap back on - this restricts fluid flow by shutting off the air and thus creating a partial vacuum.

65L

INSIDE INFORMATION: Incidentally, should you be dealing with a front drum brake, the nearest flexible hose will, in fact, actually be connected directly to the wheel cylinder. A problem here is that (normally) in order to be able to unscrew the hose from the cylinder, the hose needs also to be disconnected at its junction, on the chassis, to the metal brake pipe.

This can be 'bad news', but another trick that might avoid this problem is to first slacken the union at the cylinder, then unbolt the cylinder at the backplate and pull it clear so you can then unscrew the cylinder from the hose, rather than vice versa - usually, by the way, while you may need to slacken off manual adjusters, the brake shoes can be eased back far enough, without actually dismounting them from the backplate, to allow removal of the cylinder.

This method can come unstuck, however, if the new cylinder doesn't tighten onto the hose at more-or-less the same point as did the original: you may then still need to slacken the hose at its other end so it can be properly positioned to avoid kinking or any other undue strain during steering movement.

Generally speaking, even with independent rear suspension, the hydraulic feed pipe to a rear wheel cylinder will be a metal one, with a tube nut at the union with the cylinder. The latter might be secured to the backplate with a bolt or two, by a large C-clip, or (where it's designed to slide in the backplate) by perhaps two opposing spring clips.

65M

65M. Before attempting any dismantling, take a wire brush to the pipe union and to the bolt(s) or clips: if necessary apply penetrating oil and leave for a while beforehand. The clips can be carefully drifted out, working alternately on each leg, or maybe a large screwdriver can be used to lever them free. Note that a fixed cylinder will also probably be 'pegged' or otherwise located on the backplate.

But first that union nut must be undone, once you're sure it's free of rust and, in particular, that the adjacent length of pipe over which the nut must travel is clean and smooth. Make sure the spanner fits perfectly and once the nut is slackened be ready to work it back and forth a fraction at a time to ensure it undoes freely - what you need to beware of is thinking the nut is undoing when, in fact, nut and pipe are twisting as one, to the eventual point of breakage.

(There are, incidentally, specially produced 'tube nut' or 'flare nut' spanners, essentially a sort of split ring spanner, that will grip the union nut more effectively than the open-ended spanner that must otherwise be used).

When fitting the replacement cylinder, it can be difficult lining up the metal feed pipe and getting the union nut to pick up cleanly. It can help to do this before securing the cylinder, so it is still free to be angled a bit to align with the pipe and union. Bear in mind that if the nut tries to tighten up almost immediately, then almost certainly you are 'cross-threading' it, a danger that must be avoided at all costs - ideally, it should initially screw in some way using just your fingers.

Where a large clip is used to secure the cylinder, be prepared to wrestle awhile with the clip before it slides fully home in the groove on the cylinder - it may help to leave the bleed nipple out until the clip has been re-fitted, but note that it must be positioned so that it will not then obstruct the fitting of the nipple.

If you have an assistant, another 'trick' that can be employed to minimise the amount of bleeding required, is to have the assistant slowly and carefully press the pedal until fluid starts to escape from the still loose union, with you then tightening it while the pedal is still descending and the fluid still running, hopefully bringing with it most of the offending air.

You will still have to go through the 'bleeding' procedure. But with the compact kit available these days from the accessory shop it is not the chore it once was, and it really can be a one-man operation now, although having an assistant is still preferable.

65N. Today's bleed tube will have a one-way, 'non-return' valve in one end, so fluid can be pumped through it, but air (or expelled fluid) cannot get back in. The method is to place a ring spanner over the bleed nipple, then plug the open end of the tube over the nipple, while the valve end rests in the fluid tank which is part of the kit.

The bleed nipple needs to be cracked open just enough to allow the passage of fluid (getting it just right might take trial and error) and the brake pedal is then pressed to the floor and allowed to return in a series of rhythmic pumping strokes. Where you have assistance, one person can observe the fluid escaping into the bleed tube, typically with an infusion of air bubbles at first, while the other works the pedal and, most importantly, **keeps the master cylinder well topped up with new brake fluid.**

Whenever there is a pause in operations, perhaps for this topping-up, the nipple should be tightened while the brake pedal is still descending: you need to establish communication to this effect with your assistant. The operation continues until no more air bubbles are observed over a reasonable period and you are satisfied, having then tightened the bleed nipple, that the brake pedal is reassuringly firm and does not gradually sink to the floor when held depressed for a while.

Turning now to the brake shoes, maybe you've discovered that the friction linings are approaching their minimum permissible thickness: generally, by the way, the linings will be bonded to the shoes, but early examples were riveted to the shoes, and here renewal is also dictated if the lining is nearly flush with the heads of the rivets. Maybe the shoes are fine as far as lining thickness is concerned, but a hydraulic leak has been discovered too late, and the linings are contaminated with brake fluid.

There is no way you can salvage them, and even if it's only one shoe that's contaminated, as with disc pads, brake shoes must always be renewed as an axle set - i.e., a new pair of shoes on both offside and nearside wheels of the axle concerned.

65O. This drawing shows one typical twin-cylinder example, but if you are going to tackle shoe replacement yourself, you must study their layout on the backplate very carefully - make a sketch, or a good Polaroid photograph would be ideal. Incidentally, one benefit of the combined drum/hub design is that its removal leaves entirely open access to the brake shoes, whereas with just drum removal there remains the axle flange, which can rather impede access.

65P. You must be sure how (on rear wheels) the handbrake linkage is connected, and the same goes for an automatic brake adjustment mechanism, where fitted: This drawing typifies a layout including an auto-adjuster and a handbrake linkage (see below) where the cable enters the backplate to connect to the shoe operating level.

The handbrake linkage might be a split-pinned clevis (perhaps shrouded by a protective rubber boot) which can be disconnected now from a lever protruding through the backplate; or the handbrake cable

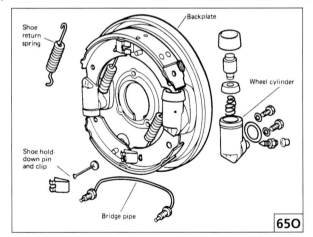

Backplate
Shoe return spring
Wheel cylinder
Shoe hold-down pin and clip
Bridge pipe
65O

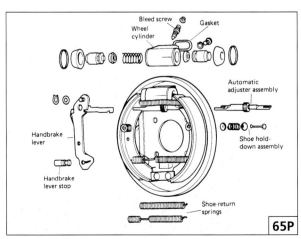

Bleed screw
Gasket
Wheel cylinder
Automatic adjuster assembly
Shoe hold-down assembly
Handbrake lever
Handbrake lever stop
Shoe-return springs
65P

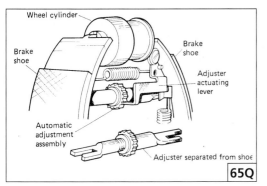

65Q

Wheel cylinder

Brake shoe

Brake shoe

Adjuster actuating lever

Automatic adjustment assembly

Adjuster separated from shoe

might continue on through the backplate, ending in a nipple slotting into a lever on one of the shoes, and which cannot easily be disconnected until that shoe has been dismounted.

65Q. An automatic adjustment mechanism might simply be an adjustable-length lever slotted between the two shoes, a not dissimilar arrangement to the toothed wheel manual adjuster described earlier in this section; here it would probably be coupled with a sprung blade fitted to one of the brake shoes - on occasion when the shoe has to move further out, because of lining wear, before it contacts the drum, on its return the blade will rotate the toothed wheel on the adjuster's screw thread, extending the lever to leave the shoes 'adjusted' nearer to the drum.

Slightly more complicated is a toothed levers set-up, again fitted to one of the shoes; here, when the shoe moves further out, spring-loading on one of the levers causes the teeth to re-mate in a position which, again, 'adjusts' the shoes nearer to the drum (see later text and illustrations).

Referring back to 65O and 65P, note into which holes on each brake shoe web the shoe pull-off springs are connected, and where such springs have a long and a short leg, note which way round they should be, and whether the spring coils face inwards or out-wards, whether the legs hook across the front of the shoe web, or vice versa, and whether one spring is heftier than the other.

65R

Often these springs stretch from one shoe to the other, but sometimes from the shoe to a hole in the backplate.

On some layouts the shoe friction lining may be bonded closer to one end of the shoe than the other, so you must remember where and which way round such shoes are fitted.

A good 'long stop' precaution, of course, is to dismantle only one backplate at a time, so you can always nip round to the other side to check how things should be!

65R. Centrally on each shoe web you should also spot either a small spring clip (as shown in Job 65O.) or what looks like a miniature coil spring, as shown here. Sitting in a groove on the clip, or in a groove in a dished washer on the little coil spring will be the flattened end of a pin. These devices constitute the brake shoe 'hold down' or 'steady' springs and since they literally pin the shoes to the backplate they must be dismantled before the shoes can be removed.

With either device, you need to steady the head of the pin behind the backplate (a finger will usually do) while you use pliers to depress the clip or dished washer and rotate until the slot which criss-crosses the groove aligns with the flattened end of the pin the clip or spring, with its washers, can then be lifted away and the pin withdrawn from the rear of the backplate.

Generally, you don't need to detach the shoe pull-off springs in order to be able to remove the shoes, although the springs may well fall off during the operation, once they are no longer under tension. But if they do need prior removal, you'll need to fashion yourself a strong hook device - perhaps a modified T-handled bradawl, or auger.

(Sometimes the problem is that the size of the axle flange precludes the shoes being pulled far enough apart to draw the spring over the flange. Note, though, that the flange may have a cut-away portion that can be positioned to alleviate the problem).

65S. There are brake kits on the market that contain all sorts of useful tools, like a flexible hose clamp and a special lever for retracting disc brake calliper pistons, and a 'shoe horn'. The latter has a split fork that straddles the central shoe web and grips the shoe snugly, and it has a longish handle to provide the leverage to pull the shoe back, against spring pressure.

INSIDE INFORMATION: A simple DIY substitute is an adjustable spanner, its jaws set to fit snugly over the shoe lining, or even a self-grip wrench. The tool would be fitted over one end of a brake shoe, its jaws and handle flat against the central shoe web.

65S

65T

It might take trial and error now to determine which end of the shoe, when levered outwards, will provide the easiest route to complete strip-down: if there is an obvious physical difference in the pull-off springs, logic might dictate that you attack the weaker end first.

65T. Typically, what you are hoping to achieve is a sequence where levering one shoe end out of its slot (in fixed abutment or wheel cylinder pis-ton) will ease the tension at the other end so it comes away easily from the slot there, whereupon the complete shoe can be relaxed inwards until the opposite shoe will lift freely from its slots - just like that!

Well, not always. And where there is an axle flange in the way it might take some juggling dexterity to pull out a shoe end and ease shoe and pull-off spring over the flange until the opposite shoe is sufficiently relaxed to be also withdrawn. And reassembly, trying to keep shoes and springs correctly hooked together, can be even more trying!

As soon as you have succeeded in removing the shoes, use a strong elastic band or tie some baling wire around the wheel cylinder to guard against accidental ejection of its piston(s). You can then thoroughly clean the backplate, not forgetting to also guard against inhalation of brake dust.

Where handbrake or automatic adjustment bits remain fitted to the old shoes, you may find, when examining the new shoes, that some of these bits must be transferred from the old to the new.

Clean up the old shoes thoroughly, so you can see exactly how and where these bits fit: they probably pivot on or through the shoe web, the pivot secured by a sprung cup washer which has to be levered off; there may be tension springs on automatic adjustment levers whose location must be noted before they are removed for transfer, with the levers, to the new shoes. In these cases there should be new cup washers in the brake shoe kit.

As we said earlier, you should still have the original installation at the opposite wheel to use as a guide, although these lever set-ups just referred to are not easily seen until the shoes are actually dismounted.

Assemble the retained original bits to the new shoes, using the copper-based grease we've mentioned previously to act as a lubricant between the moving parts. The new cup washers can either be pushed down with pliers, or an old socket of suitable smallish diameter can be used as a drift.

65U. On the toothed lever adjuster set-up mentioned, a typical procedure might be that while no specific clearance is set for the longer lever, you need to position the securing washer on the spring-tensioned shorter lever to maintain roughly 0.016 in. (sixteen thou) working clearance. Check that it returns freely when pushed against spring pressure, then mate the two levers so this shorter one is centred on the teeth of the longer one.

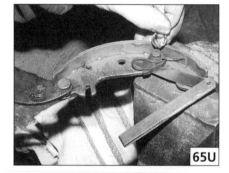
65U

(Later, when the shoes are reassembled, you may have to re-adjust this position to ensure the shoes are retracted sufficiently to enable the brake drum to be re-fitted).

A variable-length lever auto adjuster can be dismantled, cleaned, lubricated, and then screwed to its shortest length ready for reassembly.

65V. Note that some pivoted handbrake linkage levers are prone to seizure after long service, particularly those on early Ford Fiestas. Now is the time to clean them up and dose them with releasing fluid (penetrating oil) and make sure they are moving freely: afterwards you can work some of that grease into the pivot point.

Now is the time, too, to check that manual brake shoe adjusters, if fitted, are also working freely. The 'snail cam' types often fitted to front drums (also prone to seizure) can be dosed with the releasing fluid and can then be gripped by their cams (these offering better purchase than their squared protrusions) and eased to and fro: they shouldn't spin easily, but they should move smoothly. Again, if you can work some grease into them, so much the better - not only does it smooth the movement, but it also keeps damp and subsequent corrosion out.

65W. The threaded stem and component parts of the 'wedge' type manual adjusters usually fitted to rear drums can be dismantled for cleaning and greasing: if the threaded stem is initially reluctant to move, use the releasing fluid and carefully rotate it back and forth, gradually unscrewing it a bit further each time you gain a bit more free movement.

65V

When all is ready for reassembly, first smear some grease onto the raised shoe abutment points on the backplate, and also into the cylinder piston slots and the shoe fixed abutment slots - smear the shoe tips, too, but be very careful not to get grease on the friction linings. Some mechanics will wear protective gloves or temporarily stick 'cellophane' over the linings to guard against contaminating them during re-fitting.

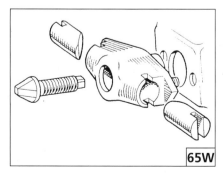

Reassembly should be more-or-less a straight reversal of the dismantling operations, although, as we have hinted, it might require some patient juggling to ensure such as handbrake linkage cross-levers, or threaded-lever type auto adjusters, and the pull-off springs, are all in their correct places. Don't forget, where appropriate, to refit internal handbrake cable linkage as you go. And, finally, don't forget the shoe hold-down springs.

65W

Once reassembly is complete, it would be a good idea to ask an assistant to gently depress the brake pedal while you check that everything moves as it should. Afterwards, also check the handbrake operation.

You may need to use a soft hammer to tap the shoes up or down in their slots to centralise them on the backplate, continuing until you find that the brake drum will slide fully home over the shoes. If any difficulty is still encountered, it can only be that an adjuster is not fully slackened off.

With the drum, or drum/hub unit properly refitted and secured, it will probably take 20 to 30 operations of the hand or footbrake to correctly re-set any automatic adjustment. Manual adjusters will have to be re-set, and re-checked once the new shoes have bedded-in, in perhaps a hundred miles or so. (See also Job 96).

12,000-mile/12-month Service

Carry out the 6000-mile/6-month service operations, plus the following:

☐ Job 66. Check valve clearances.

Many modern engines have 'hydraulic tappets' whereby the valve operating mechanism is controlled by oil pressure so that it can automatically compensate for any 'play' developing between the working parts (whether through mechanical wear or heat expansion). On older engines there is built-in 'play' and a means of adjusting it as required.

Here, again, we are talking of a pre-determined gap that is essential to the health and performance of the engine. It is a gap maintained between (basically) the valve stem (when the valve is closed) and the means employed to open the valve in order (inlet) to let the fuel mixture in or (exhaust) to let out the waste gas from the fuel combustion.

In order for the combustion and the power stroke of the piston to be as effective as possible, it is essential that during these phases the valves are firmly closed.

But if there was firm contact at all times between the valve stem and rocker arm or camshaft lobe (typical valve opening mechanisms) there is a danger that valves could be held partially open when they are supposedly shut.

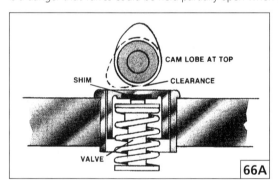

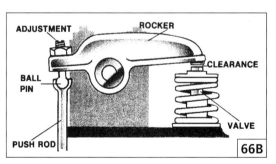

This would almost certainly occur with older design all-iron engines, where metal expansion as the engine warms up is a natural phenomenon. So in these instances a gap is essential to allow for this heat expansion.

But at the same time there must not be too large a gap, or the valve would not fully open, thus preventing, respectively, maximum fuel induction or total exhausting of the spent gases.

Paradoxically - at least to those of us more used to the commoner engines of yesteryear! - on many modern alloy cylinder head and/or block engines, the mixture of metals can lead to this heat expansion actually increasing the valve gaps!

So you can see that determining what the optimum gap should be when the engine is at normal running temperature requires quite critical calculation.

Make sure, when you look up the gap specification in your car data, that you note whether the setting is measured with the engine 'cold' (e.g., after standing overnight) or when it's 'hot' (i.e., normal running temperature).

66A. On many modern 'overhead camshaft' (ohc) engines, where the camshaft is mounted in the cylinder head directly above the valves, valve operation is directly via the camshaft lobes, and the gap is controlled (typically) by specifically sized shims in 'buckets' over the valve stems. Here, gap adjustment, when required, is achieved by adding or subtracting various thicknesses of shim.

It has to be admitted, however, that often this adjustment demands a degree of expertise and use of expensive special equipment that rather puts the operation beyond DIY capability.

Fortunately, the nicely compact set-up with fewer working parts (and thus less scope for wear and tear) employed on this type of valve mechanism, means that the need for adjustment rarely arises until comparatively high mileages, perhaps forty or fifty thousand or more.

Where the engine is simply termed 'overhead valve' (ohv) it is normally a 'pushrod' unit, whereby the camshaft, mounted lower down in the engine rather than in the cylinder head itself, operates the valves via a rod and rocker arm mechanism.

66B. The rocker arm (the bit that actually bears against the valve stem) incorporates a screw adjustment at the point of contact with the pushrod which makes gap setting fairly straightforward. There will be as many rocker arms (either sharing a common 'rocker shaft' or set on individual pedestals) as there are valves.

66C. Incidentally, there are some ohc engines where the camshaft lies alongside the valves in the cylinder head, with the shaft also employing rocker arms between itself and the valves.

Here the valve gap adjustment would be almost as straightforward as that for the ohv pushrod units, except that, with the components probably mounted lower in the head, access may be rather restricted. Sometimes, too, the gap might be measured between the cam lobe and the rocker, rather than between the valve and the rocker, while occasionally measurements for both will be given. However, since the mechanism is still relatively compact, the need for adjustment would, again, only occur after a high mileage.

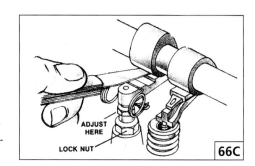

66D. Some VW and Audi vehicles require the use of a 7 mm Allen key for adjusting the gaps.

Often the specified gap will be the same for both inlet and exhaust valves, typically 0.012 in. (0.305 mm), which keeps things nice and easy.

But sometimes there will be two different measurements, say, 0.008 in. (0.22 mm) for the inlets and 0.023 in. (0.59 mm) for the exhausts - so here you need to know your exhausts from your inlets!

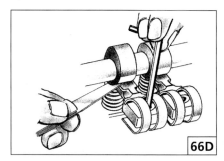

Usually, the exhaust manifold is the hefty, rusty looking chunk of roughly tubular cast-iron, bolted to the side of the cylinder head. It will have a pipe, or pipes, running down from it and leading back underneath the car. Usually alongside it, with its branches interspersed with those of the exhaust manifold, is the smoother, rather nicer looking inlet manifold, with the carburettor(s) bolted to it; sometimes the two manifolds will be on opposite sides of the engine, the latter here termed a 'crossflow' unit, and typified by the Ford Fiesta engine we have mentioned a few times.

66E. The positioning of the valves corresponds with the manifold branches, or 'ports'. For instance, you will expect to find the exhaust manifold terminating at each extremity of the cylinder head, so the first and last valves will be exhausts - and what you would also expect to find on an eight-valve, four-cylinder engine is Exhaust, Inlet, Inlet, Exhaust, Exhaust, Inlet, Inlet, Exhaust. The photograph of a partially dismantled BL 'A' Series engine (as in the Mini and Metro, for instance) is fairly typical.

On the crossflow head it is even easier to note the alignment of the respective valves with their respective manifold ports.

Obviously, this identification is best done with the valves exposed and if, indeed, your engine's valve adjustments need to be at least checked, if not (by dint of their apparent noisiness) actually requiring adjustment, then to gain access to them the 'rocker cover' (sometimes 'valve cover') will have to be removed.

Sometimes this is straightforward, whereby nothing impedes either access to it or its removal, and all you have to do is unscrew its retaining nuts or bolts and lift the cover away - you may have to tap it with a soft hammer to break its seal with its gasket and/or the top of the cylinder head, and the probably ensuing damage to the gasket underlines the fact that you need to have a replacement gasket to hand before undertaking the job.

But sometimes there may be cables, hoses, spark plug HT leads, or air cleaner assembly that need to be removed first - note carefully where all the bits fit before you clear them out of the way.

66F. Since a valve clearance must only be checked or adjusted when the valve is closed, you will need to rotate the engine to ensure that this is so. The operation will be easier with the spark plugs removed (number their leads) to relieve engine compression, and you can turn the engine either by jacking up one driving wheel and turning the wheel with, say, third gear selected (you can experiment to find which gear makes it easiest) or by using a spanner on either the crankshaft pulley nut...

66G. ...or on the generator pulley nut - here you may have to carefully lean on the drive belt to prevent it slipping.

(Note that while most engines turn clockwise in their normal direction of rotation, some - notably a few Japanese units - run anti-clockwise, so you'll need to check this beforehand).

As we said, checking or adjustment demands that the valve in question must be fully closed. There are various ways of ensuring this, some involving useful 'short cuts' evolved by mechanics of yore and some which can still save time, or you may have to go the long way round.

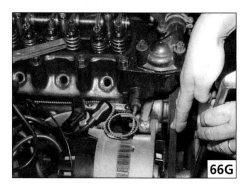

You can learn a lot about the condition of an engine from looking at the spark plugs. The following information and photographs, reproduced here with grateful thanks to NGK, show you what to look out for.

1. Good Condition

If the firing end of a spark plug is brown or light grey, the condition can be judged to be good and the spark plug is functioning at its best.

2. Carbon Fouling

Black, dry, sooty deposits, which will eventually cause misfiring and can be caused by an over-rich fuel mixture. Check all carburettor settings, choke operation and air filter cleanliness. Clean plugs vigorously with a brass bristled wire brush.

3. Oil Fouling

Oily, wet-looking deposits. This is particularly prone to causing poor starting and even misfiring. Caused by a severely worn engine but do not confuse with wet plugs removed from the engine when it won't start. If the "wetness" evaporates away, it's not oil fouling.

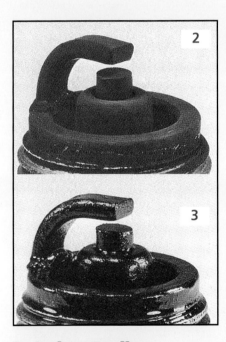

4. Overheating

When having been overheated, the insulator tip can become glazed or glossy, and deposits which have accumulated on the insulator tip may have melted. Sometimes these deposits have blistered on the insulator's tip.

5. Normal Wear

A worn spark plug not only wastes fuel but also strains the whole ignition system because the expanded gap requires higher voltage. As a result, a worn spark plug will result in damage to the engine itself, and will also increase air pollution. The normal rate of gap growth is usually around 'half-a-thou.' or 0.0006 in. every 5,000 miles (0.01 mm. every 5,000 km.).

6. Abnormal Wear

Abnormal electrode erosion is caused by the effects of corrosion, oxidation, reaction with lead, all resulting in abnormal gap growth.

7. Breakage

Insulator damage is self-evident and can be caused by rapid heating or cooling of the plug whilst out of the car or by clumsy use of gap setting tools. Burned away electrodes are indicative of an ignition system that is grossly out of adjustment. Do not use the car until this has been put right.

Of course, if it's an ohc engine you can see the camshaft - and you'll be able to see that where the peak of a camshaft lobe points directly away from the valve or rocker, then that valve must be fully closed.

On the 'pushrod' ohv engine you can't see the camshaft lobes but you can see the rockers and valves and it is these that must be observed to determine whether valves are open or closed.

Usually it is easiest, while rotating the engine, to watch a rocker arm bearing down on the valve and pushing it fully open: if you turn too far, and the rocker starts to come up again, simply turn back and then forth again until you've got it right.

The commonest 'short cut' which can be applied to many four-cylinder engines with a (cylinder numbers) 1-3-4-2 firing order is the 'rule of nine'. For example, if the engine is turned until valve number one is seen to be fully open, the gap on valve number eight can be checked/adjusted, for this valve will be fully closed; similarly, if, say, valve number six was fully open, you would check/adjust valve number three.

(On a six-cylinder engine it would be the 'rule of thirteen').

There are variations on the theme and, indeed, with experience your observation will tell you that as you turn the engine to fully open a specific valve, another will also fully open at the same time, allowing you to check/adjust two closed valves at a time, and thus cutting down on the number of rotations of the engine needing to be made.

This is much the basis of the 'rule of five' that is generally recommended for the '1-2-4-3' pushrod Ford Fiesta engine. Here, the sequence would be to turn the engine until the pair of rocker arms on, say, cylinder number four are 'on the rock' (one moving upwards, while the other is just starting to move downwards) then check/adjust the valves on cylinder number one, for both will be fully closed; similarly, with the arms rocking on cylinder number three, you would check/adjust the valves of cylinder number two.

66H

Sensibly, you would jot down the valve numbers, establish a logical engine rotation sequence, and tick the valve numbers off your list as you check/adjust them.

If you are uncertain as to whether any short cut applies to your engine, then the 'long way round' at least has the virtue of being foolproof. Here, you would turn the engine until, say, number one valve was seen to be fully open, then turn the engine one complete revolution - number one valve will now be fully closed and there should be a gap between it and its rocker arm.

66H. To check the adjustment, insert the correct value feeler gauge (e.g., 0.012 in.) into the gap: it should just, but only just, be possible to slide the feeler back and forth - it's a good idea to bear down on the other (adjuster) end of the rocker arm at the same time, to ensure all play is taken up and the gap is at its widest.

If you can't get the feeler in the gap is too small, if the feeler flops about the gap is too large.

To adjust the gap, slacken off the adjuster locknut with a ring spanner, then use a screwdriver (usually) to turn the adjuster screw up or down as required.

Some early, notably Renault, engines had flat-headed valve adjustment screws, and here you might need to fashion your own tool to suit.

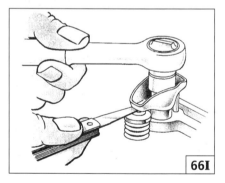
66I

66I. Others, like the Ford units mentioned earlier, have the rather easier self-locking nut adjuster.

As we said, basically it's a straightforward enough job. But to be honest we should warn you that it will take time to get used to juggling with all the tools, checking with the feeler gauge, holding the locknut still while turning the adjuster, then finally holding the adjuster still with the screwdriver while re-tightening the locknut without this action (as is its wont) messing up your adjustment!

☐ Job 67. Rocker cover gasket.

67. Thoroughly clean the inside and fit a new gasket and grommets to the rocker cover. Don't make the common mistake of over-tightening the cover - it causes leaks - just 'nip' the nuts down onto the top of the cover.

Drive the car for several miles until it reaches its normal operating temperature. Check the rocker cover again for leaks.

67

Job 68. Positive crankcase breather.

68. In addition to the filter mentioned below, on some engines there will also be a crankcase breather built into the engine, often on the valve cover and sometimes built into the oil filler cap, as shown here. Although you can't see obvious signs of wear, it does eventually become clogged and on older engines it might be beneficial to replace it as 12,000-mile intervals. If you can't spot one, your dealer should be able to tell you if and where a crankcase breather is fitted to your car.

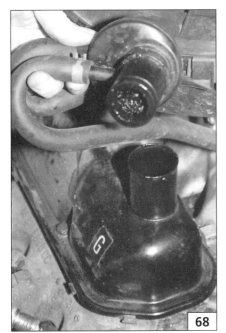

68

INSIDE INFORMATION: If your engine 'smokes' heavily through the exhaust, try replacing this valve before fearing the worst: if it's blocked, the engine can burn oil and smoke quite badly.

Job 69. Air cleaner element.

The air cleaner filter (sometimes called an element), should certainly be checked at this mileage, and probably is best actually renewed at this time also, although some schedules will say check it now and renew it at 24,000 miles. Some filter covers unclip, others need you to take out a couple of retaining screws.

69A. Generally, the element will be found beneath a lid on the air cleaner body, the lid held perhaps by a central nut, perhaps by a ring of wire clips, perhaps by the nut and clips, perhaps by three or four nuts or bolts.

69B. On older engines, with a fairly basic, inexpensive filter element such at this one, we would suggest that at this mileage you simply chuck the old and fit the new. Particularly so where old age and consequent wear and tear are causing heavy contamination of the engine fumes that are routed through the filter by the engine breathing system.

The subsequent quick contamination of the filter restricts the air intake into the fuel system, causing a condition which is akin to running with the choke in permanent operation: it soots up the spark plugs, causes rough running and leads to excessive fuel consumption (and air pollution).

Job 70. Air cleaner intake adjustment.

70. On older engines, the air intake to the lid or body may have a crude swivel adjustment

69A

69B

for summer or winter running, the adjustment usually causing the air intake to be moved nearer to (winter) or further away from (summer) the exhaust manifold; sometimes an alternative position for a length of air intake hose has the same effect. Sometimes (more sophisticated!) there may be an automatically operated flap such as the one shown here. Check that it closes the flap when the engine is started up in cold weather and opens the flap in warm weather when the engine is hot.

Job 71. Check/renew fuel filter.

71. Look in the engine compartment for a renewable 'in-line' fuel filter - when renewing, contain fuel leakage with rag. There are also 'accessory' in-line fuel filters which can be fitted into the fuel feed to the carburettor by the DIY owners.

70

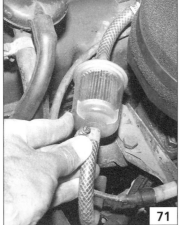

71

☐ **Job 72. Check coolant hoses.**

72A. Certainly once a year, and before adding anti-freeze as described shortly, check the condition of all coolant hoses and the security of their clips. But beware of tightening a clip on a leaking elderly hose - renewing both hose and clip is the wiser option.

72B. Examine the hoses for signs of cracking (carefully bending the straights and straightening the bends) and squeeze them to feel for any softening, perhaps caused by oil contamination. Don't overlook minor hoses, such as a feed to a water-heated inlet manifold.

Old hoses become very set in their ways, and should you need to renew one you may find that, even with its clips fully slackened off, it will be reluctant to budge.

72C. Rather than employ too much force, particularly on a radiator, where there's a high risk of fracturing the hose stub, simply slide the clip out of the way and use a strong, sharp knife to carefully slit the hose until you can open it up and peel it off the stub.

INSIDE INFORMATION: A spot of water on the rubber, preferably with an added drop of washing-up liquid, eases the cutting.

Thoroughly clean the stubs, carefully using a file and emery cloth to remove the lumpy corrosion often found on elderly alloy cooling system components.

Position new clips (preferably of the flat, 'worm-drive' type) on the new hose, ensuring their tightening screws are best placed for easy screwdriver access when the hose is fitted. A smear of washing-up fluid will help the hose slide fully home on the stubs. Tighten the clips firmly, but don't 'bury' them in the hose. (See also Job 52 and 92.)

72A

72B

☐ **Job 73. Anti-freeze.**

SAFETY FIRST!
i) Only ever remove the pressure cap when the engine is cold. ii) Take precautions to prevent anti-freeze coming into contact with the skin or eyes. If this should happen, immediately rinse with copious amounts of water - seek medical advice if necessary. iii) Never work on or touch the cooling system while the engine is running.

Once your cooling system contains anti-freeze, your car should be protected from the dangers of freezing up. However, there is the danger that topping-up the coolant with plain water will weaken the mixture. On top of that, the beneficial 'all the year round' anti-corrosion inhibitors built into the mixture will also be weakened. Therefore, the anti-freeze/coolant mixture should be changed at least every two years, while many motorists are happier to still regard the job as an annual pre-winter precaution.

72C

And, of course, if you have recently bought a secondhand vehicle it would anyway be wise to start afresh, although you could take it to a garage and ask them to check the strength of the anti-freeze for you (a simple 'dip' test) or, indeed, you could buy yourself a suitable 'hydrometer' from your local accessory shop.

If you decide to renew the mixture in your car's cooling system, first consult your handbook to determine the cooling system's capacity - alongside that data the handbook might even recommend (as a percentage) what the anti-freeze content should be.

The biggest problem now is likely to be the draining out of the old coolant.

73A. On older cars, drain taps on both the radiator...

73A

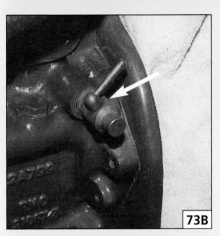

73B

73B. ...and the engine cylinder block are easily identifiable and easily found: the tap on that partially dismantled 'A' Series engine may be replaced by just a screwed plug on later engines.

73C. Other older cars might have some sort of drain tap or a plug in the bottom of the radiator, but you might be hard put to find anything in the way of a drain plug, let alone an identifiable tap, on the engine block.

73D. For the vast majority of cars, the only way to let coolant out will be to temporarily disconnect the bottom hose from the radiator.

*INSIDE INFORMATION: Every few years, you may want to flush the system. Disconnect top and bottom hoses **from the radiator.** Insert the garden hose, first into the bottom of the rad., then into the end of the bottom hose (heater taps open), stuffing the gap with a piece of rag. Then flush again from above. You'll be surprised by how much muck you'll shift - and your heater could even work better afterwards!*

It also used to be widely held that anti-freeze causes leaks. Basically, it doesn't, it finds them: having a lower surface tension than ordinary water, it can flow out through gaps tight enough normally to contain the plain water - hence the need to check hoses and clips before adding anti-freeze.

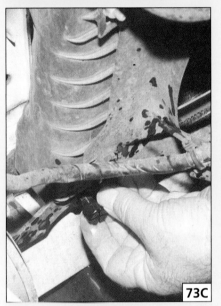

73C

Anyway, when you do drain, by whatever means, first remove the filler cap (from radiator or expansion tank, as appropriate) to aid the flow - and, of course, never attempt the job until the coolant has cooled sufficiently for there to be no danger of scalding yourself. Heater controls should be set to 'Hot', incidentally, so that this part of the system is also open to coolant flow.

73E. When you are happy that the system is ready to receive its fresh anti-freeze, it is usually more sensible (as already mentioned) to first add the required quantity of neat anti-freeze, then top up with clean water as required to bring the coolant content to its correct level. If the radiator has a cap, pour the anti-freeze into the radiator...

73F. ...if the radiator doesn't have a cap, pout the anti-freeze into the expansion tank.

Should you be unlucky enough to find that a little less than your proposed amount of neat anti-freeze fills the system to capacity, you might be able to console yourself (bearing in mind our average winter temperatures) that a 25 per cent solution should protect down to minus 13 degrees Centigrade, 33 per cent down to minus 19 and 50 per cent down to minus 36 degrees Centigrade - it's very unlikely that you won't have got enough in to give yourself peace of mind - but do remember the higher anti-corrosion requirements of some engines. Check your handbook.

73D

Pour slowly and carefully, so the system gradually fills without danger of air-locks building up anywhere. When the level appears to be correct, start the engine and let it run for a few minutes with the filler cap off. Note that as the thermostat starts to open (evidenced by the radiator top hose warming up) any minor air-locks may disperse, causing the level to drop back a bit - when feeling the top hose, beware the fan or other moving parts.

Top up as required, stop the engine, and if all appears to be well replace the cap.

73E

73F

In the unlikely event of a serious air-lock, however, this could cause the level to rise and threaten an overflow, so be ready to replace the cap and switch off immediately.

Such an air-lock is often betrayed by one or more of the heater hoses still feeling cold (or at best only luke warm) even when the engine has been run for a while - the heater hoses should warm up and, indeed, feel quite hot some while before that top hose will start to feel warm. Again, take all due precautions when feeling the hoses.

73G. A crude, but effective way of dispersing this air-lock, having now stopped the engine, is to first loosen the heater return hose at its junction within the engine compartment - this is the one that probably leads to the radiator bottom hose stub or an adjacent stub at the water pump.

73H. On some cars it might be easier to detach it at the heater unit connection, but make sure it is the return hose, and not the feed hose from the engine.

Start the engine, then either detach the hose completely from its stub or displace it sufficiently to allow the coolant to escape in quantity.

As soon as coolant does flow freely, push the hose fully home on its stub while the engine is still running - both heater hoses should now start to feel significantly hot, showing that the air-lock has been dispersed.

Stop the engine and re-tighten the hose securing clip. Mop up any coolant spillage remaining within the engine compartment - note that (as we have warned previously) anti-freeze can be injurious to paintwork if not washed off immediately.

(It goes without saying that this operation demands great care to both avoid moving parts and guard against scalds from the coolant, or burns from a hot exhaust).

Top up the coolant level now as required, and check it after every run for the next few days to ensure that it has settled down, and that no leaks are occurring anywhere.

Retain a water/anti-freeze mix of the recommended concentration for any topping-up required in the future.

☐ Job 74. Battery terminals.

Provided the battery is kept clean and dry and is not topped-up over generously, its terminals should also remain clean and sound unless a generator fault is causing it to be over-charged, with consequent heavy 'gassing' from the cells.

74A. Generally speaking, it is electrolyte spillage or this excess vapour which leads to the 'fungal growth' noted on the terminals of neglected batteries as seen here. It is a condition which, as well as the highly corrosive effect on nearby metals, such as the battery clamp and the battery tray, also causes poor electrical contact. In the extreme, the starter may fail to operate, or all electrics may apparently fail.

74B. If you have inherited a secondhand vehicle suffering from this problem, simply pouring hot water over the terminals and any other affected parts, such as the battery strap or clamp, and the battery tray, will usually prove remarkably effective. Take care that you don't pour the hot water into the battery cells or onto nearby vulnerable components and ensure all of the corrosive 'fuzz' is washed away from the car's bodywork.

74C. If necessary, the hot water treatment can be followed by use of a wire brush and/or emery cloth to bring the battery lead connectors and the battery terminal posts back to clean and bright condition. A slim knife blade or half-round file can be useful to clean inside the lead connectors.

Be very careful to guard against 'short circuits' when working on battery terminals. The gas ensuing from the cells, particularly when the battery is being charged, is extremely explosive and ignition by a careless spark can cause a truly horrific battery explosion.

74D

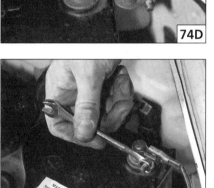

74E

(A typical cause of accidental short-circuit is the bristles of a wire brush touching a battery terminal and a battery strap at the same time, or, similarly, a spanner being used to tighten a terminal nut also touching this strap or the car bodywork).

74D. Once all connections are clean and dry, a smear of petroleum jelly, a proprietary battery jelly or copper-impregnated grease, will guard against further corrosion and help to maintain good electrical contact. Badly affected metals should be treated with a rust killer and re-painted. Smear lightly inside; more heavily over all the outside of the terminals.

74E. Finally, terminal connections should be tight but not 'murdered'.

☐ Job 75. Brake servo filter.

75. The brake servo helps you to apply pressure to the brakes, making the brake pressure lighter than it otherwise would have been. If your car's brake servo has a filter of the type shown arrowed here, you can service it yourself, as follows. Remove the five screws securing the air valve cover and blow out the filter area. This can be done with a foot-pump, then replace the filter.

> **SAFETY FIRST!**
> **If your brake servo filter is not of this type, this is a SPECIALIST SERVICE job since dismantling may be involved. Have it done, however, because otherwise the efficiency of the brake servo will gradually diminish.**

75

Around the Car

☐ Job 76. Toolkit and jack.

Inspect the toolkit, wipe tools with an oily rag to stop them rusting and lubricate the jack, checking that it works smoothly. Also, check that the spare wheel retaining bolt hasn't rusted in. Remove it and lubricate the threads with a dab of grease.

☐ Job 77. Lamp seals.

Remove the side light/indicator lenses, particularity the front indicators, and ensure that the seals are effective. If water has been getting in to the lights, remove the bulbs and smear a light coating of petroleum jelly inside the bulb holder to prevent rust. Renew the seal.

☐ Job 78. Alarm remote units.

If an alarm is fitted to your car, replace the battery in each alarm sender unit. Otherwise, as was once found by the publisher of this book, it is all too easy to be banished from your own car, if the battery 'dies' at an inopportune moment. Like in France. With the shops shut...

☐ Job 79. Adjust headlights.

It is possible to adjust your own headlights but not with sufficient accuracy. Badly adjusted headlights can be very dangerous if they don't provide you, the driver, with a proper view of the road ahead or they dazzle oncoming drivers. Older drivers and those with poor eyesight can become disorientated when confronted with maladjusted headlights. **SPECIALIST SERVICE** Have the work carried out for you by a garage with beam measuring equipment. Any MoT testing station in the UK will be properly equipped.

☐ Job 80. Check front hubs bearings.

> **SAFETY FIRST!**
> **Do not go beneath the car when it is supported only by a jack.**

80

Wear is often associated with a humming noise or squealing from the affected wheel, easing off when cornering with the load on the opposite wheel.

80. Jack up each wheel in turn and rock it vertically to check for 'play' - if an assistant depresses the brake pedal and the play disappears, then it was in the wheel bearing. If the bearing is still smooth and quiet, but just slack and is adjustable, refer to the procedure described in Job 65. Noisy bearings, or slack non-adjustable bearings must be replaced - **SPECIALIST SERVICE**.

☐ Job 81. Check steering and suspension.

Some jobs, like the greasing pertaining to older vehicles, and tyre checks and steering rack gaiter checks, we have mentioned earlier, and these should, of course, be repeated at this 12,000-mile service.

But while many steering and suspension components are sealed for life and non-adjustable, there are other aspects which may not figure specifically in your car's official service schedule, but which we believe demand regular attention.

Not least of these is the checking for wear and tear that can spot impending trouble before it becomes an expensive, and possibly dangerous, failure.

Rack gaiters and steering balljoints (track rod ends) we've dealt with, but not dissimilar are the rubber shrouds on suspension swivels. Again, split boots can let lubricant out and abrasive dirt in.

You might need some assistance to help you check for wear - for instance, someone to rock the steering wheel to and fro (road wheels on the ground) while you watch underneath for signs of lost movement in the linkage from the steering rack (or box) to the wheels: obviously, more than an inch or so steering wheel movement with no resultant movement of the road wheels points to quite significant wear somewhere.

81A

81A. Don't overlook the possibility of wear in any universal joints in the steering column itself, or of slackness in rack (or box) mounting points.

Further checks can be made with the front wheels off the ground. Now each wheel in turn can be gripped by hand and rocked vertically to show up wear in suspension balljoints, or the king-pins of older cars.

It can also show up worn wheel bearings - see Job 80.

Worn steering balljoints may be detected by rocking each road wheel laterally.

Check that suspension dampers are firmly mounted - See Job 89.

Look for signs of severe rust or cracks in coil or leaf springs.

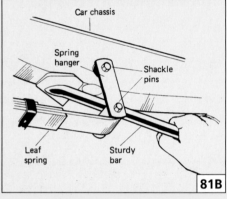
Car chassis

Spring hanger

Shackle pins

Leaf spring

Sturdy bar

81B

81B. Where you can, and particularly at the spring hangers and shackle pins on the rear leaf springs of older cars, see if you can emulate the MoT Tester by judiciously applying a hefty lever to check for unwanted movement.

Finally, note that judder at the steering wheel while driving along may result from seriously worn strut-type front suspension; or it might result from out-of-balance front or rear wheels.

A reputable tyre dealer should re-balance any wheel to which he has fitted a new tyre, but the problem can be self-induced if, for any reason, you swap wheels around, or, perhaps, fit the spare.

An irregularly worn (and possibly noisy) tyre is often the first sign of a steering or suspension fault - see also the tyre wear illustrations in the 'MoT' section later in this book.

☐ Job 82. Exhaust emissions.

SPECIALIST SERVICE - Have a properly equipped garage carry out an exhaust gas emissions check, especially for carbon monoxide (CO) and unburned hydrocarbons.

Under the Car

☐ Job 83. Inspect Underside.

83A. When dry, inspect the underside of the car for rust and damage. Renew paint, underbody sealant and wax coating locally as necessary. Old-fashioned bitumen type underseal goes brittle and comes loose anyway, this only makes the problem worse. Water will soon penetrate this area and form a breeding ground for corrosion. Scrape off any such loose underseal and paint on wax coating in its place, when dry.

83A

83B. Use a screwdriver or light hammer to test for loose, flaking or rusty metal.

Job 84. Clear drain holes.

Check and clear the drain holes in sills, doors, boot and those in the lower sill.

Job 85. Check gearbox oil.

Whereas most modern, front-wheel drive cars feature a 'transmission' unit that houses both the gears and the final drive in close proximity, sharing a common supply of oil, older, rear-wheel drive cars have a separate gearbox and final drive (rear axle).

The notable exceptions to the norm of either yesterday or today, are, of course, the front-wheel drive units that have variously worn BMC, BLMC, BL, Leyland and, nowadays, Rover badges - for here (the Mini being the most famous of them all) the gearbox and final drive not only share the same oil supply, they share it, too, with the engine!

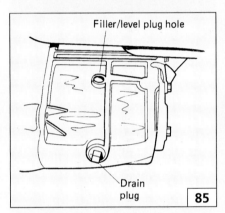

With the modern 'transmission' unit, the usual recommendations are that the oil level is checked, and if necessary topped up, at 12,000-miles/12 months (see later) and, perhaps, changed at 24,000-miles/2-years: that said, some such units do not have a drain plug and so an oil change is neither considered (by the car maker) to ever be necessary, nor is it catered for.

It's a different story with the older separate gearboxes and rear axles, however. Here, earlier schedules (e.g., the original handbook) specified checking the levels at 3000-mile/3-month intervals and draining and refilling at 6000-mile/6-month intervals.

Unless frequent, wet oily patches are noted on the ground where the vehicle has been parked, denoting significant leakage, a 6000-mile/6-month level check, as recommended in more recent years, should be adequate. If the car is a real 'golden oldie', you might feel happier changing the oil at this period.

85. With the gearbox, look for a filler/level plug on its side, perhaps roughly half-way up and probably on the nearside. If fitted, the drain plug will be square, hexagon or recess-headed and screwed into the bottom of the unit. In all cases, as with the engine sump plug, use only the correct tool for the job.

Clean away dirt from the filler/level plug area before unscrewing and removing the plug: check with a finger that oil is up to the level of the plug hole.

If topping-up is required, you'll need to know what type/grade of oil should be used. The gearbox might use engine oil, or a specific 'gear oil'.

Job 86. Check rear axle oil.

REAR WHEEL DRIVE CARS ONLY.

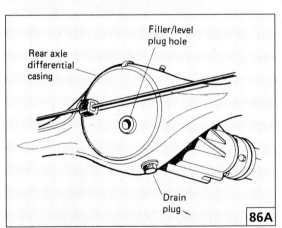

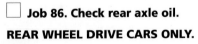

86A. Look for the filler/level plug on the differential casing rear face.

Generally, these transmission oils will be sold in plastic 'squeezee' bottles, supplied with a flexible extension tube, and topping-up (particularly where access is restricted) is easiest using these bottles and tubes. Squeeze in oil until the level overflows, then replace the plug and mop up as necessary.

An 'EP' (extreme pressure) or Hypoid gear oil may be recommended typically 'EP90'.

As with the engine oil, draining, when required, is best done after a short run, when the warmed-up oil will flow more easily.

86B. While you're in the vicinity, grease the handbrake cross-shaft (where fitted) and linkages.

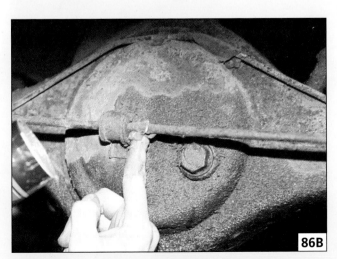

☐ **Job 87. Check transaxle oil.**

FRONT WHEEL DRIVE CARS ONLY.
Unlike the separate gearbox and final drive (rear axle) units of older cars, most newer cars will have an integral gearbox and final drive (a 'transaxle' unit) housed in a single transmission casing and sharing a common supply of oil.

Generally, there will be no provision for draining and refilling (i.e., no drain plug in the bottom of the casing) but there will be a filler/level plug in the side of the casing. If your car is fitted with automatic transmission, you will also have to remove and clean a filter, washing it out in white spirit - see your handbook for its location.

To check the level, simply unscrew the plug and insert a finger (not when the unit is hot!) and ensure the oil comes up to the bottom edge of the plug hole.

87. If necessary, add gear oil as specified in your handbook, replacing the plug when the level starts to overflow from the plug hole. Mop up any spillage.

☐ **Job 88. Check telescopic dampers.**

88. Check for fluid leaks from the telescopic dampers. If they are seeping, it will show from the top shroud. Also check the condition of the damper mounting bushes. If they appear soft, spreading - or non-existent! - fit new ones. Faulty dampers must be replaced, always in pairs.

In the case of early Minis and other BL cars, leaking hydrolastic displacers will normally be associated with a loss in the ride height. Any faults with these is outside the normal servicing procedures and is definitely **SPECIALIST SERVICE**.

☐ **Job 89. Check lever-arm dampers.**

89. If you have an older car fitted with lever-arm dampers (they were often an integral part of the front suspension) they should also be checked for leaks and security - but note that some had provision for topping-up with damper, or shock-absorber oil.

☐ **Job 90. Clutch hydraulics.**

Check the clutch flexible pipe for perishing or cracks. It is unlikely that the rigid pipe will have corroded because of its location in the engine bay.

90. Peel back the rubber boot from the slave cylinder (the Mini example is easily reached!) and take a look for fluid leaks. Spotting a trickle early can save total failure later.

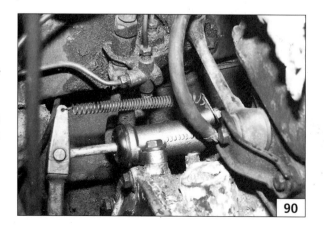

24,000 MILES - OR EVERY TWO YEARS, whichever comes first

It is important to remember, of course, that your DIY servicing doesn't just stop when you have completed everything listed for the 12,000-mile/12-month Service!

Obviously, common sense has to be used as far as time expiry is concerned. For instance, taking an extreme example, if for some reason the car wasn't used for 12 months, having just had a 12,000-mile/12-month service, while it might be prudent to change the engine oil again, you wouldn't expect to have to re-check or re-adjust the valve clearances! But there are some jobs which will crop up only at long-term or high-mileage intervals, perhaps only once during your ownership of the car.

91

Job 91. Radiator pressure cap.

91. Renew the radiator pressure cap - the rubber seal perishes and the spring weakens over time which reduces the pressure in the system which, in turn, allows the coolant to boil at a lower temperature.

Job 92. Refill cooling system.

Every two years, the coolant should be drained from the cooling system, discarded and then replenished with fresh. This is to ensure that the anti-corrosion properties of the coolant are retained and you should also take the opportunity to flush out the cooling system, getting rid of any debris that may have built up in there. Before draining down the cooling system, turn the heater tap on to the fully open position and remove the filler cap. As mentioned in Job 73, it is not easy to completely drain the coolant from some modern cars - sometimes the bottom hose will have to be disconnected.

INSIDE INFORMATION If the bottom hose has not been off for two years, the chances are that it will stick and need replacing anyway. Be prepared and have a spare hose on hand.

SAFETY FIRST!
Only drain down the system when the engine is cold.

Before refilling the system flush it through. With all filler caps still off, put a garden hose into the car's bottom hose and try to plug the gap between the small bore of the garden hose and the larger bore of the bottom hose (good luck!). Turn on the tap and run the water until no more sediment comes out of the filler plug. Try turning the heater tap on and off so that the flow through the heater surges through it and helps to clear sediment from the heater itself. Now take the garden hose out and insert it into the bottom stub of the radiator and flush that out in the same way.

In order to refill the system, first check your car's cooling system capacity, then follow the coolant/anti-freeze advice detailed in Job 73.

SAFETY FIRST!
i) Keep your hands away from the cooling fan and belts. Stop the engine and carefully remove the radiator cap and top-up. Now you should run the engine, getting it up to full operating temperature and revving the engine rapidly on several occasions so that the water pump pushes the water round the system and removes any air locks. Wait for, the water to cool down fully and then check the level once again. Take care to check the water levels after the first time you use the car on the road, allowing the water to cool down fully before taking the radiator pressure cap off again, see Job 73 for further details. ii) Only drain down the system when the engine is cold.

Job 93. Check brake discs.

You would need a micrometer to measure the thickness of the brake discs, and compare the reading with the minimum permitted for your car. If the discs are still thick enough but badly scored, you may be able to have an engineering shop skim them down for you. (Provide them with the minimum permissible thickness and ask them to check the discs run true before spending money on them.) But check their price against the cost of replacement discs. (See also Job 64).

☐ Job 94. Brake callipers.

94. *INSIDE INFORMATION: See Job 64 for information on removing and replacing disc brake pads. When it is time to check the front pads, remove them and wash and scrape out the brake callipers, with proprietary brake cleaner, to reduce the risk of brake squeal and seizure.*

SAFETY FIRST!
Never use any other substance when cleaning out brakes and note the safety hazards when working with brake dust referred to in Chapter 1, Safety First!

☐ Job 95. Renew brake fluid.

95. This shot shows an experienced mechanic preparing to bleed the brakes. **SPECIALIST SERVICE.** Unless you are an experienced, trained mechanic, it is essential that you either have a garage or a trained mechanic carry out this work for you, or if you carry out the work yourself with the assistance of a workshop manual, to have a trained mechanic check your car before using it on the road.

SAFETY FIRST!
If this work is carried out in an unskilled manner, the car's braking system could fail totally. If the work is not carried out at all, the system could also fail. Brake fluid deteriorates over a period of time - it absorbs moisture from the air and then, under heavy braking, the water can turn to vapour, creating an air lock in the braking system and leaving the car without brakes. It is best to invest in the cost of having this work carried out by your local authorised dealer.

☐ Job 96. Check brake drums.

SPECIALIST SERVICE. After long, arduous service and especially on older cars, it is advisable to have a specialist examine the thickness and depth of wear of all brake drums. If excessively scored or worn thin (maximum diameter is often cast into the drum itself) or if *any* sign of cracking is found, have it replaced.

INSIDE INFORMATION: your specialist should tap the drum, suspended on a piece of string or a hook, to see if it rings true. If it produces a flat note, the drum is cracked and must be replaced: don't use the car until it has been done. (See also Job 65).

36,000 MILES - OR EVERY THREE YEARS, whichever comes first

☐ Job 97. Renew camshaft belt.

97. If your car is fitted with an overhead-camshaft engine, with belt-driven camshaft, your handbook will probably recommend renewing it every so often. Every 24,000 miles is usually considered to be a *very* careful change point; we recommend a maximum of every 50,000 miles, unless the maker of your car recommends a shorter interval.

☐ Job 98. Renew ATF.

Automatic transmission fluid is usually changed ever three years, but the interval might be less, depending on the model of car; consult your handbook. Also check to see if this is a DIY job. There will invariably be a filter of filters to wash out in white spirit and usually, if you buy new washers for the drain and filter plugs, this is not difficult to do. If it becomes more involved than that, make this a **SPECIALIST SERVICE** job.

Do check your car's handbook to see if there are any other 'long term' service requirements special to your model of car.

CHAPTER 6
REPAIRING BODYWORK BLEMISHES

However well you look after your car, there will always be the risk of car park accident damage - or even worse! The smallest paint chips are best touched up with paint purchased from your local auto. accessory shop. If your colour of paint is not available, some auto. accessory shops offer a mixing scheme or you could look for a local paint factor in Yellow Pages. Take your car along to the paint factor and have them match the colour and mix the smallest quantity of cellulose paint that they will supply you with.

Larger body blemishes will need the use of body filler. You should only use a filler with a reputable name behind it, such as Isopon P38 Easy Sand and that's what we used to carry out this repair.

SAFETY FIRST!
Always wear plastic gloves when working with any make of filler, before it has set. Always wear a face mask when sanding filler and wear goggles when using a power sander.

4.1

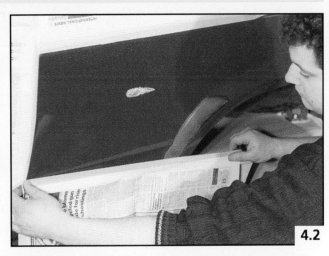

4.2

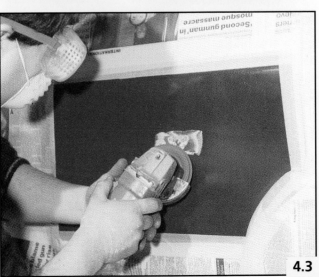

4.3

4.1 The rear of this car has sustained a nasty gash - the sort of damage for which you will certainly need to use body filler.

4.2 The first stage is to mask off. Try to find "natural" edges such as body mouldings or styling stripes and wherever you can, mask off body trim rather than having to remove it.

4.3 Isopon recommend that you remove all paint from the damaged area and for about 1 in. around the damaged area. Roughen the bare metal or surface with coarse abrasive paper - a power sander is best - and wipe away any loose particles. If you have access to professional spirit wipe, so much the better and the whole area should now be wiped down. If not, wipe over the area with white spirit (mineral spirit) and then wash off with washing-up liquid in water - not car wash detergent.

4.4 Use a piece of plastic on which to mix the filler and hardener, following the instructions on the can.

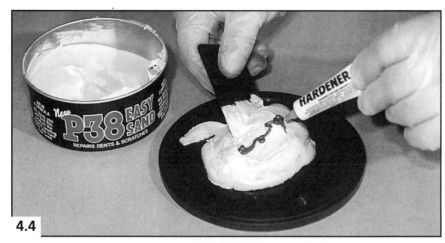

4.4

4.5 Mix the filler and hardener thoroughly until the colour is consistent and no traces of hardener can be discerned. It's best to use a piece of plastic or metal rather than cardboard because otherwise, the filler will pick up fibres from the surface of the card.

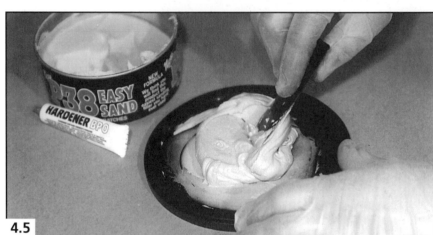

4.5

4.6 You can now spread the filler evenly over the repair.

4.7 If the damage is particularly deep, apply the paste in two or more layers, allowing the filler to harden before adding the next layer. The final layer should be just proud of the level required, but do not overfill as this wastes paste and will require more time to sand down. (Courtesy Isopon)

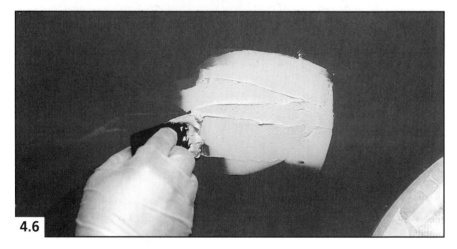

4.6

4.7

4.8 It is essential when sanding down that you wrap the sanding paper around a flat block. You can see from the scratch marks that the repair has been sanded diagonally in alternate directions until the filler is level with the surrounding panel but take care not to go deeply into the edges of the paint around the repair.

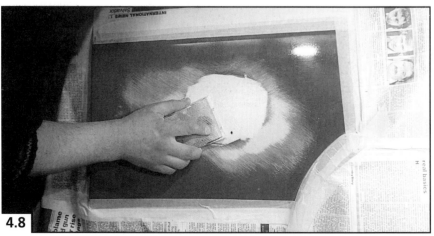

4.8

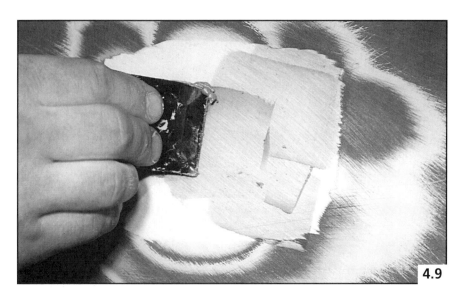

4.9 There will invariably be small pin holes even if, as in this case, the right amount of filler was applied first time. Use a tiny amount of filler scraped very thinly over the whole repair, filling in deep scratches and pin holes and then sanding off with a fine grade of sand paper - preferably dry paper rather than wet-or-dry because you don't want to get water on to the bare filler - until all of the core scratches from the earlier rougher sanding have been removed.

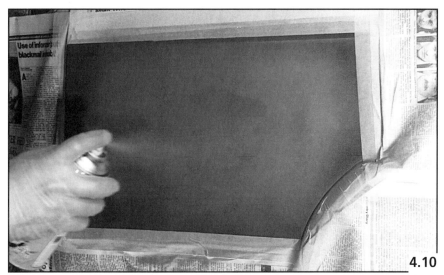

4.10 You can now use an aerosol primer to spray over the whole area of the repair but preferably not right up to the edges of the masking tape...

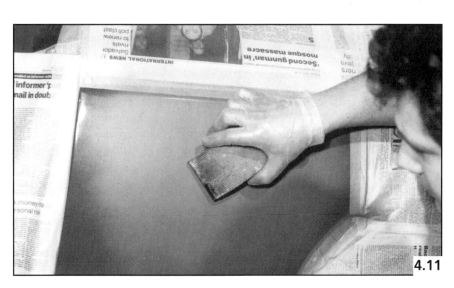

4.11 ...and you can now use wet-or-dry paper, again on a sanding block, to sand the primer paint since the Isopon is now protected from the water by the paint. If you do apply paint right up to the edge of the tape, be sure to 'feather' the edges of the paint, once it has dried off thoroughly (usually next day) so that the edges blend in smoothly to the surrounding surface, with no ridges.

SAFETY FIRST!
Always wear an efficient mask when spraying aerosol paint and only work in a well-ventilated area, well away from any source of ignition, since spray paint vapour, even that given off by an aerosol, is highly flammable. Ensure that you have doors and windows open to the outside when using aerosol paint but in cooler weather, close them when the vapour has dispersed otherwise the surface of the paint will "bloom", or take on a milky appearance. In fact, you may find it difficult to obtain a satisfactory finish in cold and damp weather.

4.12 Before starting to spray, ensure that the nozzle is clear. Note that the can must be held with the index finger well back on the aerosol button. If you let your finger overhang the front of the button, a paint drip can form and throw itself on to the work area as a paint blob. This is most annoying and means that you will have to let the paint dry, sand it down and start again.

4.13 One of the secrets of getting a decent coat of paint which doesn't run badly is to put a very light coat of spray paint on to the panel first, followed by several more coats, allowing time between each coat for the bulk of the solvent to evaporate. Alternate coats should go horizontally, followed by vertical coats as shown on the inset diagram.

4.14 If carried out with great care and skill, this type of repair can be virtually invisible. After allowing about a week for the paint to dry, you will be able to polish it with a light cutting compound, blending the edges of the repair into the surrounding paintwork.

4.12

Do note that if your repairs don't work out first time and you have to apply more paint on top of the fresh paint that you have already used, allow a week to elapse otherwise there is a strong risk of pickling or other reactions taking place. Also note that a prime cause of paint failure is the existence of silicone on the surface of the old paint before you start work. These come from most types of polish and are not all that easy to remove. Thoroughly wipe the panel down with white spirit before starting work and wash off with warm water and washing-up liquid to remove any further traces of the polish and the white spirit - but don't use the sponge or bucket that you normally use for washing the car otherwise you will simply introduce more silicones onto the surface!

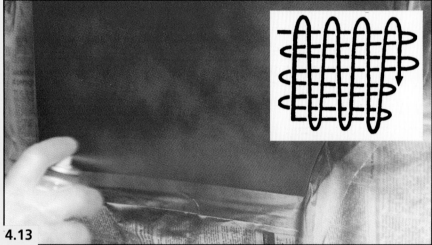

4.13

4.15 We are grateful to W. David & Sons Ltd, the makers of Isopon for their assistance with this section of the book and to CarPlan for their supply of the aerosol paints featured here. Isopon P38 is available in several different sizes of container and can easily be matched to the size of the repair that you have to carry out and all of the products shown here are readily available from high street motorists' stores.

4.14

4.15

CHAPTER 7 - FAULT FINDING

This Chapter aims to help you to overcome the main faults that can affect the mobility or safety of your car. It also helps you to overcome the problem that has affected most mechanics - amateur and professional - at one time or another... Blind Spot Syndrome!

It goes like this: the car refuses to start one damp Sunday morning. You decide that there must be no fuel getting through. By the time you've stripped the fuel pump, carburettor, fuel lines and "unblocked" the fuel tank, it's time for bed. And the next day, the local garage finds that your main HT lead has dropped out of the coil! Something like that has happened to most of us!

Don't leap to assumptions: if your engine won't start or runs badly, if electrical components fail, follow the logical sequence of checks listed here and detailed overleaf, eliminating each "check" (by testing, not by "hunch") before moving on to the next. Remember that the great majority of failures are caused by electrical or ignition faults: only a minor proportion of engine failures come from the fuel system, follow the sequences shown here - and you'll have better success in finding that fault. Before carrying out any of the work described in this Chapter please read carefully *Chapter 1 Safety First!*

ENGINE WON'T START.

1. Starter motor doesn't turn.

2. Starter motor turns slowly.

3. Starter motor noisy or harsh.

4. Starter motor turns engine but car will not start. See 'Ignition System' box.

5. Is battery okay?

6. Can engine be rotated by hand?

7. Check battery connections for cleanliness/tightness.

8. Test battery with voltmeter.

9. Have battery 'drop' test carried out by specialist.

10. If engine cannot be rotated by hand, check for mechanical seizure of power unit, or pinion gear jammed in mesh with flywheel - 'rock' car backwards and forwards until free, or apply spanner to square drive at front end of starter motor.

11. If engine can be rotated by hand, check for loose electrical connections at starter, faulty solenoid, or defective starter motor.

12. Battery low on charge or defective - recharge and have 'drop' test carried out by specialist.

13. Internal fault within starter motor - e.g. worn brushes.

14. Drive teeth on ring gear or starter pinion worn/broken.

15. Main drive spring broken.

16. Starter motor securing bolts loose.

IGNITION SYSTEM.

(Carry out the following checks as appropriate. For example, some vehicles have contact breaker ignition while the majority have electronic ignition.)

17. Check for spark at plug (remove plug and prop it with threads resting on bare metal of cylinder block). Do not touch plug or lead while operating starter.

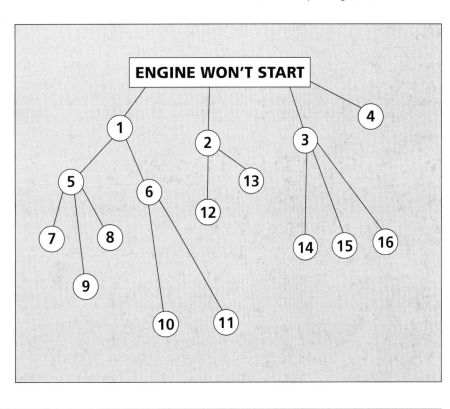

ENGINE WON'T START

18. If no spark present at plug, check for spark at contact breaker points when 'flicked' open (ignition 'on'). Double-check to ensure that points are clean and correctly gapped, and try again.

19. If spark present at contact breaker points, check for spark at central high tension lead from coil.

20. If spark present at central high tension lead from coil, check distributor cap and rotor arm; replace if cracked or contacts badly worn.

21. If distributor cap and rotor arm are okay, check high tension leads and connections - replace leads if they are old, carbon core type suppressed variety.

22. If high tension leads are sound but dirty or damp, clean/dry them.

23. If high tension leads okay, check/clean/dry/re-gap sparking plugs.

24. Damp conditions? Apply water dispellant spray to ignition system.

25. If no spark present at contact breaker points, examine connections of low tension leads between ignition switch and coil, and from coil to contact breaker (including short low-tension lead within distributor).

26. If low tension circuit connections okay, examine wiring.

27. If low tension wiring is sound, is condenser okay? If in doubt, fit new condenser.

28. If condenser is okay, check for spark at central high tension lead from coil.

29. If no spark present at central high tension lead from coil, check for poor high tension lead connections.

30. If high tension lead connections okay, is coil okay? If in doubt, fit new coil.

31. If spark present at plug, is it powerful or weak? If weak, see '27'.

32. If spark is healthy, check ignition timing.

33. If ignition timing is okay, see 'Ignition System' box. (see 36).

FUEL SYSTEM.

34. Check briefly for fuel at feed pipe to carb. See 37. If no fuel present at feed pipe, is petrol tank empty? (Rock car and listen for 'sloshing' in tank, as well as looking at gauge).

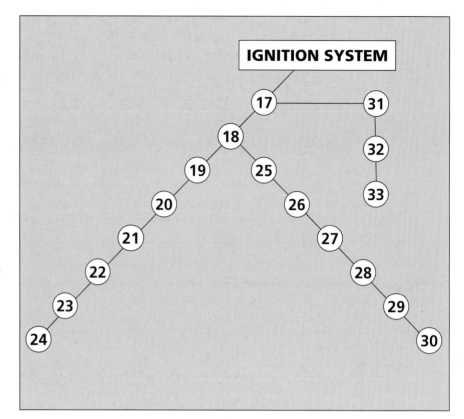

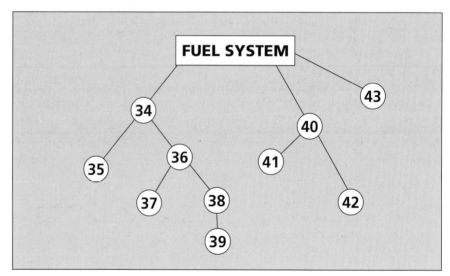

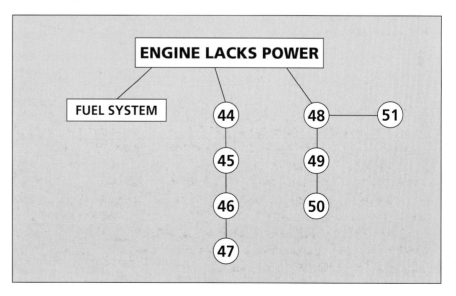

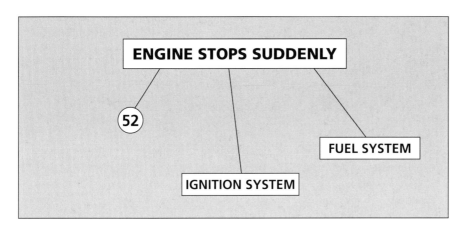

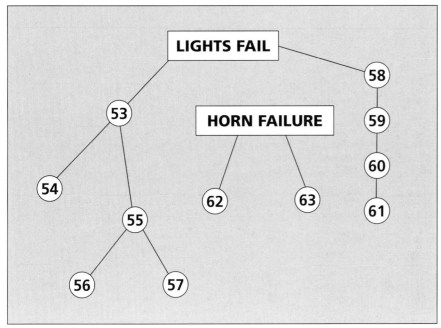

35. If tank is empty, replenish!

36. If there is petrol in the tank but none issues from the feed pipe from pump to carburettor, check that the small vent hole in the fuel filler cap is not blocked and causing a vacuum.

37. Check for a defective fuel pump. With outlet pipe disconnected AND AIMED AWAY FROM HOT EXHAUST COMPONENTS, ETC. as well as your eyes and clothes, and into a suitable container, turn the engine over (manual pump) or switch on ignition (electric pump) and fuel should issue from pump outlet.

38. If pump is okay, check for blocked fuel filter or pipe, or major leak in pipe between tank and pump, or between pump and carb.

39. If the filter is clean and the pump operates, suspect blocked carburettor jet(s) or damaged/sticking float, or incorrectly adjusted carburettor.

40. If fuel is present at carburettor feed pipe, remove spark plugs and check whether wet with unburnt fuel.

41. If the spark plugs are fuel-soaked, check that the choke is operating as it should and is not jammed 'shut'. Other possibilities include float needle valve(s) sticking 'open' or leaking, float punctured, carburettor incorrectly adjusted or air filter totally blocked. Clean plugs before replacing.

42. If the spark plugs are dry, check whether the float needle valve is jammed 'shut'.

43. Check for severe air leak at inlet manifold gasket or carburettor gasket. Incorrectly set valve clearances.

ENGINE LACKS POWER.

44. Engine overheating. Check oil temperature gauge (where fitted). Low oil pressure light may come on.

45. Air cleaner intake thermostat not opening/closing at the correct temperatures. Replace or free-off as necessary.

46. If thermostat okay, check oil level. BEWARE - DIPSTICK AND OIL MAY BE VERY HOT.

47. If oil level okay, check for slipping fan belt, cylinder head gasket 'blown', partial mechanical seizure of engine, blocked or damaged exhaust system.

48. If engine temperature is normal, check cylinder compressions.

49. If cylinder compression readings low, add a couple of teaspoons of engine oil to each cylinder in turn, and repeat test. If readings don't improve, suspect burnt valves/seats.

50. If compression readings improve after adding oil as described, suspect worn cylinder bores, pistons and rings.

51. If compression readings are normal, check for mechanical problems, for example, binding brakes, slipping clutch, partially seized transmission, etc.

ENGINE STOPS SUDDENLY.

52. Check for sudden ingress of water /snow onto ignition components, in adverse weather conditions. Sudden failure is almost always because of an ignition fault. Check for simple wiring and connection breakdowns.

LIGHTS FAIL.

53. Sudden failure - check fuses.

54. If all lamps affected, check switch and main wiring feeds.

55. If not all lamps are affected, check bulbs on lamps concerned.

56. If bulbs appear to be okay, check bulb holder(s), local wiring and connections.

57. If bulb(s) blown, replace!

58. Intermittent operation, flickering or poor light output.

59. Check earth (ground) connections(s).

60. If earth(s) okay, check switch.

61. If switch okay, check wiring and connections.

HORN FAILURE.

62. If horn does not operate, check fuse, all connections (particularly earths/grounds) and cables. Remove horn connections and check/clean. Use 12v test lamp to ascertain power getting to horn.

63. If horn will not stop(!), disconnect the horn and check for earthing of horn button or cable between button and horn unit and the wiring and contacts in the horn switch and steering column tube.

FUEL GAUGE PROBLEMS.

64. Gauge reads 'empty' - check for fuel in tank.

65. If no fuel present, replenish!

66. If fuel is present in tank, check for earthing of wiring from tank to gauge, and for wiring disconnections. On many models, gauge is mechanical - check cable is sound from gauge to tank and that it is not trapped.

67. Gauge permanently reads 'full', regardless of tank contents. Check wiring and connections as in '66'.

68. If wiring and connections all okay, sender unit/fuel gauge defective.

69. With wiring disconnected, check for continuity between fuel gauge terminals. Do NOT test gauge by short-circuiting to earth. Replace unit if faulty.

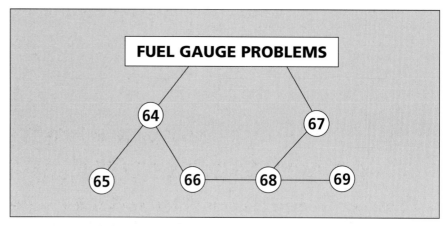

If gauge is okay, disconnect wiring from tank sender unit and check for continuity between terminal and case. Replace sender unit if faulty.

SUPPLEMENTARY INFORMATION - DIESEL ENGINES

The following fault finding chart covers in detail only those parts of the system that can be checked at home. If a simple solution is not found. it will be necessary to call on the services or a Land Rover specialist or diesel injection specialist.

1. *No fuel.* If the tank is allowed to run dry. the system will have to be bled as described in Chapter 5.

2. *Fuel blockages* from the tank to the pump can be checked at home. It is most important that any checks on the fuel system from the pump to the engine are carried out by a specialist. The high pressure means that a blockage is unlikely but also means that there is a safety hazard involved in working on this part of the system.

3. *Air in fuel system.* Bleed as described in Chapter 5.

4. *Glow plugs (cold engine).* These only fail after a very high mileage and usually one at a time. The usual symptom is an engine which starts, misfires and smokes badly until warmed up Proper checking is usually SPECIALIST SERVICE

5. *Slow cranking speed* can be caused by bad electrical connections or a flat battery.

6. *Worn bores* will affect a diesel engine more severely than a petrol engine so a worn out engine is less likely to start or run properly.

7. *Stop control faulty.* Check that the solenoid in the stop control "clicks" when the solenoid is switched on or off, in which case you can assume it is working. If a manually-controlled valve is fitted. check that the valve at the pump operates when the knob is moved. Otherwise this is also SPECIALIST SERVICE.

8. *Injection pump faulty.* SPECIALIST SERVICE

9. *Injector faulty.* SPECIALIST SERVICE

10. *Injector feed pipe leaking.* SPECIALIST SERVICE

	1	2	3	4	5	6	7	8	9	10
Engine will not start	✓	✓	✓	✓	✓	✓	✓	✓		
Engine will not stop							✓			
Engine misfires	✓					✓		✓	✓	✓
Excessive (black) smoke from exhaust								✓	✓	

CHAPTER 8
GETTING THROUGH THE MOT

This Chapter is for owners in Britain whose vehicles need to pass the 'MoT' test. The Test was first established in 1961 by the then Ministry of Transport and it attempts to ensure that vehicles using British roads reach minimum standards of safety. Approximately 40 per cent of vehicles submitted for the test fail it, but many of these failures could be avoided by knowing what the vehicle might 'fall down on', and by taking appropriate remedial action before the test 'proper' is carried out.

It is true that the scope of the test has been considerably enlarged in the past few years, with the result that it is correspondingly more difficult to be sure that your vehicle will reach the required standards. In truth, however, a careful examination of the relevant areas, perhaps a month or so before the current certificate expires, will highlight components which require attention, and enable any obvious faults to be rectified before you take the vehicle for the test.

GETTING AHEAD

It is also worth noting that a vehicle can be submitted for a test up to a month before the current certificate expires - if the vehicle passes, the new certificate will be valid until one year from the day of expiry of the old one, provided that the old certificate is produced at the time of the test.

KEEPING UP TO DATE

In view of the numbers of additions to the test in recent years, it is MOST IMPORTANT that UK owners check for themselves that legislation has not changed since this book was written. Also, non-UK owners should obtain information on the legal requirements in their own territory - and act accordingly.

MAKING A GOOD IMPRESSION

If your vehicle is muddy or particularly dirty (especially underneath) it would be worth giving it a thorough clean a day or two before carrying out the inspection so that it has ample time to dry. Do the same before the real MoT test. A clean vehicle makes a better impression on the examiner, who can refuse to test a vehicle which is particularly dirty underneath.

On the other hand, a clean vehicle makes a better impression and it will help the examiner to see what he is supposed to be examining. Generally, this will work in the owner's favour. For example, if a component or an area of underbody or chassis is particularly difficult to examine due to a build-up of oily dirt etc., and if the examiner is in doubt about its condition, he is entitled to fail that component because it was not possible for him to conclude that it reached the required standard. Had it been clean, it might well have been tested, and passed!

MoT testers do not dismantle assemblies during the test but you may wish to do so during your pretest check-up for a better view of certain wearing parts, such as the rear brake shoes for example. See *Chapter 5, Service Intervals Step-by-Step* for information on how to check the brakes.

BUYING AND SELLING

This chapter provides a procedure for checking your vehicle's condition prior to its official MoT test. The same procedure could be equally useful to UK and non-UK owners alike when examining vehicles prior to purchase (or sale for that matter). However, it must be emphasised that the official MoT certificate should not be

SAFETY FIRST!
The MoT tester will follow a set procedure and we will cover the ground in a similar way, starting inside the vehicle, then continuing outside, under the bonnet, underneath the vehicle etc. When preparing to go underneath the vehicle, do ensure that it is jacked on firm level ground and then supported on axle stands or ramps which are adequate for the task. Wheels which remain on the ground should have chocks in front of and behind them, and while the rear wheels remain on the ground, the hand brake should be firmly ON. For most repair and replacement jobs under your vehicle these normal precautions will suffice. However, the vehicle needs to be even more stable than usual when carrying out these checks. There must be no risk of it toppling off its stands while suspension and steering components are being pushed and pulled in order to test them. Read carefully Chapter 1, Safety First! for further important information on raising and supporting a vehicle above the ground.

regarded as any guarantee of the condition of a vehicle. All it proves is that the vehicle reached the required standards, in the opinion of a particular examiner, at the time and date it was tested.

PASS THE MoT!

The aim of this chapter is to explain what is actually tested on a vehicle and (if it is not obvious) how the test is done. This should enable you to identify and eliminate problems before they undermine the safety or diminish the performance of your vehicle and long before they cause the expense and inconvenience of a test failure.

TOOL BOX

Dismantling apart, few tools are needed for testing. A light hammer is useful for tapping panels underneath the vehicle when looking for rust. If this produces a bright metallic noise, then the area being tapped is solid metal. If the noise produced is dull, the area contains rust or filler. When tapping sills and box sections, listen also for the sound of debris (that is, rust flakes) on the inside of the panel. Use a screwdriver to prod weak parts of panels. This may produce holes of course, but if the panels have rusted to that extent, you really ought to know about it. A strong lever (such as a tyre lever) can be useful for applying the required force to suspension joints etc. when assessing whether there is any wear in them.

You will need an assistant to operate controls and perhaps to wobble the road wheels while you inspect components under the vehicle.

AGE OF THE VEHICLE - A DEFINITION

Two more brief explanations are required before we start our informal test. Firstly, the age of the vehicle determines exactly which lights, seat belts and other items it should have. Frequently in the next few pages you will come across the phrase "Cars first used ..." followed by a date. A vehicle's "first used date" is either its date of first registration, or the date six months after it was manufactured, whichever was earlier. Or, if the vehicle was originally used without being registered (such as a vehicle which has been imported to the U.K. or an ex-H.M. Forces model, etc.) the "first used date" is the date of manufacture.

RUST AND LOAD-BEARING AREAS

Secondly, there must not be excessive rust, serious distortion or any fractures affecting certain prescribed areas of the bodywork. These prescribed areas are load-bearing parts of the bodywork within 30 cm (12 in.) of anchorages or mounting points associated with testable items such as seat belts, brake pedal assemblies, master cylinders, servos, suspension and steering components and also body mountings. Keep this rule in mind while inspecting the vehicle, but remember also that even if such damage occurs outside a prescribed area, it can cause failure of the test. Failure will occur if the damage is judged to reduce the continuity or strength of a main load-bearing part of the bodywork sufficiently to have an adverse effect on the braking or steering.

The following notes are necessarily abbreviated, and are for assistance only. They are not a definitive guide to all the MoT regula-

tions. It is also worth mentioning that the varying degrees of discretion of individual MoT testers can mean that there are variations between the standards as applied. However, the following points should help to make you aware of the aspects which will be examined. Now, if you have your clipboard, checklist and pencil handy, let's make a start...

THE 'EASY' BITS

Checking these items is straightforward and should not take more than a few minutes - it could avoid an embarrassingly simple failure...

LIGHTS

Within the scope of the test are headlamps, side and tail lights, brake lamps, direction indicators, and number plate lamps (plus rear fog lamps on all cars first used on or after 1 April, 1980, and any earlier cars subsequently so equipped, and also hazard warning lamps on any vehicle so fitted). All must operate, must be clean and not significantly damaged; flickering is also not permitted. The switches should also all work properly. Pairs of lamps should give approximately the same intensity of light output, and operation of one set of lights should not affect the working of another - such trouble is usually due to bad earthing.

Indicators should flash at between 60 and 120 times per minute. Rev the engine to encourage them, if a little slow (although the examiner might not let you get away with it! Otherwise, renew the (inexpensive) flasher unit and check all wiring and earth connections.

Interior 'tell-tale' lamps, such as for indicators, rear fog lamps and hazard warning lamps should all operate in unison with their respective exterior lamps.

Head light aim must be correct - in particular, the lights should not dazzle other road users. An approximate guide can be obtained by shining the lights against a vertical wall, but final adjustment may be necessary by reference to the beam checking machine at the MoT station. Most testers will be happy to make slight adjustments where necessary but only if the adjusters work make sure before you take the vehicle in that they are not seized solid!

Reflectors must be unbroken, clean, and not obscured - for example, by stickers.

WHEELS AND TYRES

Check the wheels for loose nuts, cracks, and damaged rims. Missing wheel nuts or studs are also failure points, naturally enough!

There is no excuse for running on illegal tyres. The legal requirement is that there must be at least 1.6 mm. of tread depth remaining, over the 'central' three-quarters of the width of the tyre all the way around. From this it can be deduced that there is no legal requirement to have 1.6 mm. (1/16 in.) of tread on the 'shoulders' of the tyre, but in practice, most MoT stations will be reluctant to pass a tyre in this condition. In any case, for optimum safety - especially 'wet grip' - you would be well advised to change tyres when they wear down to around 3 mm. (1/8 in.) or so depth of remaining tread.

Visible 'tread wear indicator bars', found approximately every nine inches around the tread of the tyre, are highlighted when the tread reaches the critical 1.6 mm. point.

Tyres should not show signs of cuts or bulges, rubbing on the bodywork or running gear, and the valves should be in sound condition, and correctly aligned.

Cross-ply and radial tyre types must not be mixed on the same axle, and if pairs of cross-ply and radial tyres are fitted, the radials must be on the rear axle.

WINDSCREEN

The screen must not be damaged (by cracks, chips, etc.) or obscured so that the driver does not have a clear view of the road. Permissible size of damage points depends on where they occur. Within an area 290 mm. (nearly 12 in.) wide, ahead of the driver, and up to the top of the wiper arc, any damage must be confined within a circle less than 10 mm. (approx. 0.4 in.) in diameter. This is increased to 40 mm. (just over 1.5 in.) for damage within the rest of the screen area swept by the wipers.

WASHERS AND WIPERS

The wipers must clear an area big enough to give the driver a clear view forwards and to the side of the vehicle. The wiper blades must be securely attached and sound, with no cracks or 'missing' sections. The wiper switch should also work properly. The screen washers must supply the screen with sufficient liquid to keep it clean, in conjunction with the use of the wipers.

MIRRORS

Your vehicle must have at least two, one of which must be on the driver's side. The mirrors must be visible from the driver's seat, and not be damaged or obscured so that the view to the rear is affected. Therefore cracks, chips and discolouration can mean failure.

HORN

The horn must emit a uniform note which is loud enough to give adequate warning of approach, and the switch must operate correctly. Multi-tone horns playing 'in sequence' are not permitted, but two tones sounding together are fine.

SEAT SECURITY

The seats must be securely mounted, and the sub-frames should be sound.

NUMBER (REGISTRATION) PLATES

Both front and rear number plates must be present, and in good condition, with no breaks or missing numbers or letters. The plates must not be obscured, and the digits must not be repositioned (to form names, for instance).

VEHICLE IDENTIFICATION NUMBERS (VIN)

Vehicles first used on or after 1 August, 1980 have to have a clearly displayed VIN - Vehicle Identification Number (or old-fashioned 'chassis numbers' for older cars) which is plainly legible. See *Chapter 2, Buying Spares* for the correct location on your vehicle.

EXHAUST SYSTEM

The entire system must be present, properly mounted, free of leaks and should not be noisy - which can happen when the internal baffles fail. 'Proper' repairs by welding, or exhaust cement, or bandage are acceptable, as long as no gas leaks are evident. Then again, common sense, if not the MoT, dictates that exhaust bandage should only be a very short-term emergency measure. For safety's sake, fit a new exhaust if yours is reduced to this!

SEAT BELTS

Seat belts must be in good condition (i.e. not frayed or otherwise damaged), and the buckles and catches should also operate correctly. Inertia reel types, where fitted, should retract properly.

Belt mountings must be secure, with no structural damage or corrosion within 30 cm. (12 in.) of them.

MORE DETAILS

You've checked the easy bits - now it's time for the detail! Some of the 'easy bits' referred to above are included here, but this is intended as a more complete check list to give your vehicle the best possible chance of gaining a First Class Honours, MoT Pass!

INSIDE THE VEHICLE

1. The steering wheel should be examined for cracks and for damage which might interfere with its use, or injure the driver's hands. It should also be pushed and pulled along the column axis, and also up and down, at 90 degrees to it. This will highlight any deficiencies in the wheel and upper column mounting/bearing, and also any excessive end float, and movement between the column shaft and the wheel. In the case of the smaller number of cars with steering boxes, rotate the steering wheel in both directions to test for free play at the wheel rim - this shouldn't exceed approximately 75 mm (3.0 in.), assuming a 380 mm (15 in.) diameter steering wheel. Look, too, for movement in the steering column couplings and fasteners (including the universal joint), and visually check their condition and security. They must be sound, and properly tightened.

In the case of cars with steering racks, rotate the steering wheel in both directions to test for free play at the wheel rim - this shouldn't exceed approximately 13 mm. (0.5 in.), assuming a 380 mm. (15 in.) diameter steering wheel. Look, too, for movement in the steering column, couplings and fasteners, and visually check their condition and security. They must be sound, and properly tightened.

In both cases where the steering wheel is larger or smaller the amount of permissible free play should be raised or lowered accordingly.

2. Check that the switches for headlamps, sidelights, direction indicators, hazard warning lights, wipers, washers and horn, appear to be in good working order and check that the tell-tale lights or audible warnings are working where applicable.

3. Make sure that the windscreen wipers operate effectively with blades that are secure and in good condition. The windscreen washer should provide sufficient liquid to clear the screen in conjunction with the wipers.

GETTING THROUGH THE MOT

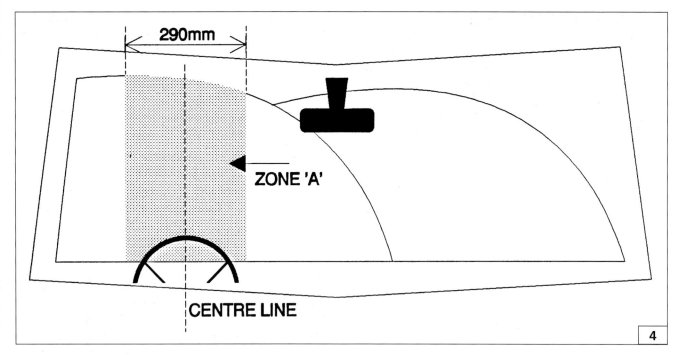

4

4. Check for windscreen damage, especially in the area swept by the wipers. From the MoT tester's point of view, Zone A is part of this area, 290 mm (11.5 in.) wide and centred on the centre of the steering wheel. Damage to the screen within this area should be capable of fitting into a 10 mm (approx. 0.4 in.) diameter circle and the cumulative effect of more minor damage should not seriously restrict the driver's view. Windscreen stickers or other obstructions should not encroach more than 10 mm (approx 0.4 in.) into this area. In the remainder of the swept area the maximum diameter of damage or degree of encroachment by obstructions is 40 mm (approx. 1.6 in.) and there is no ruling regarding cumulative damage. Specialist windscreen companies can often repair a cracked screen for a lot less than the cost of replacement. Moreover, the cost of repair is often covered by comprehensive insurance policies without excess.

5. The horn control should be present, secure and readily accessible to the driver, and the horn should be loud enough to be heard by other road users. Gongs, bells and sirens are not permitted (except as part of an anti-theft device) and multi- tone horns (which alternate between two or more notes) are not permitted at all. On cars first used after 1 August 1973, the horn should produce a constant, continuous or uniform note which is neither harsh nor grating.

6. There must be one exterior mirror on the driver's side of the vehicle and either an exterior mirror fitted to the passenger's side or an interior mirror. The required mirrors should be secure and in good condition.

7. Check that the hand brake operates effectively without coming to the end of its working travel. The lever and its mechanism must be complete, securely mounted, unobstructed in its travel and in a sufficiently good condition to remain firmly in the "On" position even when knocked from side to side. The 30 cm rule applies in the vicinity of the hand brake lever mounting.

8. The foot brake pedal assembly should be complete, unobstructed, and in a good working condition, including the pedal rubber

(which should not have been worn smooth). There should be no excessive movement of the pedal at right angles to its normal direction. When fully depressed, the pedal should not be at the end of its travel. The pedal should not feel spongy (indicating air in the hydraulic system), nor should it tend to creep downwards while held under pressure (which indicates an internal hydraulic leak).

9. Seats must be secure on their mountings and seat backs must be capable of being locked in the upright position.

10. The law requires all models to be fitted with seatbelts for the driver and both front passengers. These have to be three-point lap and diagonal belts with at least three anchorage points for the driver and nearside passenger, and a lap belt only for the centre passenger position. Rear seat belts are a requirement for vehicles first used after 31 March 1987. Examine seat belt webbing and fittings to make sure that all are in good condition and that anchorages are firmly attached to the vehicle's structure. Locking mechanisms should be capable of remaining locked, and of being released if required, when under load. Flexible buckle stalks (if fitted) should be free of corrosion, broken cable strands or other weaknesses. Note that any belts fitted which are not part of a legal requirements may be examined by the tester but will not form part of the official test.

11. On inertia reel belts, check that on retracting the belts the webbing winds into the retracting unit automatically, albeit with some manual assistance to start with.

12. Note the point raised earlier regarding corrosion around seat belt anchorage points. The MoT tester will not carry out any dismantling here, but he will examine floor mounted anchorage points from underneath the vehicle if that is possible.

13. Before getting out of the vehicle, make sure that both doors can be opened from the inside.

OUTSIDE THE VEHICLE

14. Before closing the driver's door check the condition of the inner sill. Usually the MoT tester will do this by applying finger or thumb pressure to various parts of the panel while the floor covering remains in place. For your own peace of mind, look beneath the sill covering, taking great care not to tear any covering. Then close the driver's door and make sure that it latches securely and repeat these checks on the nearside inner sill and door.

Now check all of the lights, front and rear, (and the number plate lights) while your assistant operates the light switches.

15. As we said earlier, you can carry out a rough and ready check on head lamp alignment for yourself, although it will certainly not be as accurate as having it done for you at the MoT testing station. Drive your vehicle near to a wall, as shown. Check that your tyres are correctly inflated and the vehicle is on level ground.

Draw on the wall, with chalk:
• a horizontal line about 2 metres long, and at same height as centre of head lamp lens.

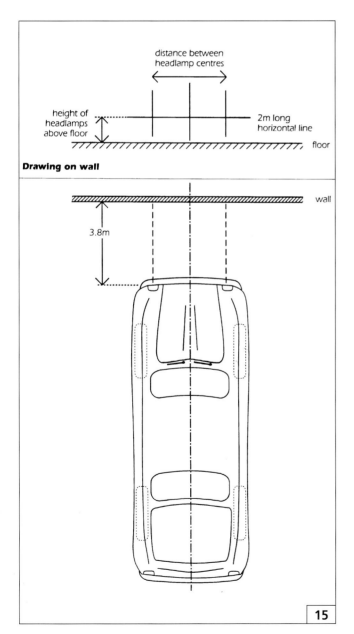

Drawing on wall

distance between headlamp centres

height of headlamps above floor

2m long horizontal line

floor

wall

3.8m

15

• two vertical lines about 1 metre long, each forming a cross with the horizontal line and the same distance apart as the head lamp centres.
• another vertical line to form a cross on the horizontal line, midway between the others.

Now position your vehicle so that:
• it faces the wall squarely, and its centre line is in line with centre line marked on the wall.
• the steering is straight.
• head light lenses are 5.0 metres (16 ft.) from the wall.

Switch on the headlamps' 'main' and 'dipped' beams in turn, and measure their centre points. You will be able to judge any major discrepancies in intensity and aim prior to having the beams properly set by a garage with beam measuring equipment.

Headlamps should be complete, clean, securely mounted, in good working order and not adversely affected by the operation of another lamp, and these basic requirements affect all the lamps listed below. Headlamps must dip as a pair from a single switch. Their aim must be correctly adjusted and they should not be affected (even to the extent of flickering) when lightly tapped by hand. Each head lamp should match its partner in terms of size, colour and intensity of light, and can be white or yellow.

16. Side lights should show white light to the front and red light to the rear. Lenses should not be broken, cracked or incomplete.

17. Vehicles first used before 1 April 1986 do not have to have a hazard warning device, but if one is fitted, it must be tested, and it must operate with the ignition switch either on or off. The lights should flash 60-120 times per minute, and indicators must operate independently of any other lights.

18. Check your stop lights. They should produce a steady red light when the foot brake is applied.

19. There must be two red rear reflectors - always fitted by the manufacturers, of course! - which are clean, and securely and symmetrically fitted to the vehicle.

20. Your vehicle must have one rear fog lamp fitted to the centre or offside of the vehicle. It must comply with the basic requirements (listed under headlamps) and emit a steady red light. Its tell-tale lamp, inside the vehicle, must work to inform the driver that it is switched on.

21. There must be registration number plates at the front and rear of the vehicle and both must be clean, secure, complete and unobscured. Letters and figures must be correctly formed and correctly spaced and not likely to be misread due to an uncovered securing bolt or whatever. The year letter counts as a figure. The space between letters and figures must be at least twice that between adjacent letters or figures.

22. Number plate lamps must be present, working, and not flickering when tapped by hand, just as for other lamps. Where more than one lamp or bulb was fitted as original equipment, all must be working.

The MoT tester will examine tyres and wheels while walking around the vehicle and again when he is underneath it.

23. Front tyres should match each other and rear tyres should match each other, both sets matching in terms of size, aspect ratio and type of structure. For example, you must never fit tyres of different sizes or types, such as cross-ply or radial, on the same 'axle' - both front wheels counting as 'on the same axle' in this context. Cross-ply or bias belted tyres should not be fitted on the rear axle, with radials on the front, neither should cross-ply tyres be fitted to the rear, with bias belted tyres on the front.

24. Failure of the test can be caused by a cut, lump, tear or bulge in a tyre, exposed ply or cord, a badly seated tyre, a re-cut tyre, a tyre fouling part of the vehicle, or a seriously damaged or mis-aligned valve stem which could cause sudden deflation of the tyre. To pass the test, the grooves of the tread pattern must be at least 1.6 mm deep throughout a continuous band comprising the central three-quarters of the breadth of tread, and round the entire outer circumference of the tyre.

We are grateful to Dunlop/SP Tyres for all of the following photographs and information in this section.

24A. Modern tyres have tread wear indicators built into the tread groves (usually about eight of them spread equidistantly around the circumference). These appear as continuous bars running across the tread when the original pattern depth has worn down to 1.6 mm. There will be a distinct reduction in wet grip well before the tread wear indicators start to show, and you should replace tyres before they get to this stage, even though this is the legal minimum in the UK.

24B. Lumps and bulges in the tyre wall usually arise from accidental damage or even because of faults in the tyre construction. You should run your hand all the way around the side wall of the tyre, with the vehicle either jacked off the ground, or moving the vehicle half a wheels revolution, so that you can check the part of the tyre that was previously resting on the ground. Since you can't easily check the insides of the tyres in day-to-day use, it is even more important that you spend time carefully checking the inside of each tyre - the MoT tester will certainly do so! Tyres with bulges in them must be scrapped and replaced with new, since they can fail suddenly, causing your vehicle to lose control.

24C. Abrasion of the tyre side wall can take place either in conjunction with bulging, or by itself, and this invariably results from an impact, such as the tyre striking the edge of a kerb or a pothole in the road. Once again, the tyre may be at imminent risk or failure and you should take advice from a tyre specialist on whether the abrasion is just superficial, or whether the tyre will need replacement.

24D. All tyres will suffer progressively from cracking, albeit in most cases superficially, due to the effects of sunlight. If old age has caused the tyres on your vehicle to degrade to this extent, replace them.

TWI

NEW TYRE

ILLEGAL TYRE

24A

24B

24E. If the outer edges of the tread are worn noticeably more than the centre, the tyres have been run under inflated which not only ruins tyres, but causes worse fuel consumption, dangerous handling and is, of course, illegal.

Over-inflation causes the centre part of the tyre to wear more quickly than the outer edges. This is also illegal but in addition, it causes the steering and grip to suffer and the tyre becomes more susceptible to concussion damage.

24E

24C

24F

24F. Incorrect wheel alignment causes one side of the tyre to wear more severely than the other. If your vehicle should ever hit a kerb or large pothole, it is worthwhile having the wheel alignment checked since this costs considerably less than new front tyres!

25. Road wheels must be secure and must not be badly damaged, distorted or cracked, or have badly distorted bead rims (perhaps due to "kerbing"), or loose or missing wheel nuts, studs or bolts.

24D

26. Check the bodywork for any sharp edges or projections, caused by corrosion or damage, which could prove dangerous to other road users, including pedestrians.

27. Check that the fuel cap fastens securely and that its sealing washer is neither torn nor deteriorated, or its mounting flange damaged sufficiently to allow fuel to escape (for example, while the vehicle is cornering).

UNDER THE BONNET

28. The vehicle should have a Chassis Number or Vehicle Identification Number fitted to the bodywork. This can be on a plate secured to the vehicle or, etched or stamped on the bodywork. See *Chapter 2, Buying Spares* for more information.

29. Check the steering rack or box for security by asking your assistant to turn the steering wheel from side to side (with the road wheels on the ground) while you watch what happens under the bonnet. Then, check for free play in the steering assembly as a whole. This is done by turning the steering wheel from side to side as far as possible without moving the road wheels - and measuring how far the steering wheel can be moved in this way. More than 75 mm (approx. 3 in.) of free play, on a steering box system, or 13 mm (approx. 0.5 in.), on a steering rack, at the perimeter of the steering wheel, due to wear in the steering components, is sufficient grounds for a test failure. Note that the 75 mm criterion is based on a steering wheel diameter of 380 mm (approx 15 in) and will be less for smaller steering wheels. Also check for the presence and security of retaining and locking devices in the steering column assembly.

30. While peering under the bonnet, check that hydraulic master cylinders and reservoirs are securely mounted and not severely corroded or otherwise damaged. Ensure that the caps are present, that fluid levels are satisfactory and that there are no fluid leaks.

31. Also check that the brake servo is securely mounted and not damaged or corroded to an extent that would impair its operation. Vacuum pipes should be sound, that is, free from kinks, splits and excessive chafing and not collapsed internally.

32. Still under the bonnet have a thorough search for evidence of excessive corrosion, severe distortion or fracture in any load bearing panelling within 30 cm (12 in.) of important mounting points such as the master cylinder/servo mounting, front suspension mountings etc.

UNDER THE VEHICLE - FRONT END

33. SAFETY FIRST!
On some occasions there is no alternative but for your assistant to sit in the vehicle whilst you go beneath. Therefore: 1) Place the ramps as well as axle stands beneath the vehicle's structure so that it cannot fall. 2) Don't allow your assistant to move vigorously or get in or out of the vehicle while you are beneath it. If either of these are problematical, DON'T CARRY OUT THIS CHECK - leave it to your garage.

34. Have an assistant turn the steering wheel from side to side while you watch for movement in the steering mechanism. Make sure that the rack or box mountings are secure, that the ball joints show no signs of wear and that the ball joint dust covers are in sound condition. Ensure that all split pins, locking nuts and so on are in place and correctly fastened, throughout the steering and suspension systems.

35. With all four wheels on the ground, push down firmly a couple of times on each front wing of the vehicle, then let go at the bottom of the stroke. The vehicle should return to approximately its original level within two or three strokes. Continuing oscillations will earn your vehicle a 'failure' ticket for worn front shockers!

36. With the vehicle raised, spin each wheel in turn, listening for roughness in the bearings. There must be none.

37. Under the vehicle, check the condition of the front springs. Wearing goggles, use a stuff brush to clean off the mud and other debris so that you don't miss a hidden 'crack'. Make sure that all suspension mountings are sound.

38. Inspect the shock absorbers. Their upper shrouds (outer casing) tend to rust. Any sign of leaks will cause failure of the test - look for weeping hydraulic fluid just below the lower edge of the upper shroud. Take a firm grip on the upper and lower shroud in turn with both hands and try to twist the damper to check for deterioration in the top and bottom mounting bushes.

UNDER THE VEHICLE - REAR SUSPENSION

39. Check the operation of the rear shock absorbers in the same way as the front (item 35).

40. Check the rear wheel bearings as described in item 36.

41. Check the condition of the rear springs and suspension components as described in item 37.

42. Check the condition of the rear shock absorbers as described in item 38.

BRAKES

43. The MoT brake test is carried out on a special 'rolling road' set-up, which measures the efficiency in terms of percentage. For the foot brake, the examiner is looking for 50 per cent; the hand brake must measure 25 per cent. Frankly, without a rolling road of your own, there is little that you can do to verify whether or not your vehicle will come up to the required figures. What you can do, though, is carry out an entire check of the brake system, which will also cover all other aspects the examiner will be checking, and be as sure as you can that the system is working efficiently.

IMPORTANT! See *Chapter 5, Service Intervals, Step-by-Step* for important information, including *SAFETY FIRST!* information before working on your vehicle's brakes.

44. The MoT examiner will not dismantle any part of the system, but you can do so. So, take off each front wheel in turn, and examine as follows:

DISC BRAKES

Check the front brake discs themselves, looking for excessive grooving or crazing, the calliper pistons/dust seals (looking for signs of fluid leakage and deterioration of the seals), and the brake pads - ideally, replace them if less than approximately 3 mm. (1/8th in.) friction material remains on each pad.

DRUM BRAKES

Remove each brake drum and check the condition of the linings (renew if worn down to anywhere near the rivet heads), the brake drum (watch for cracking, ovality and serious scoring, etc.) and the wheel cylinders. Check the cylinder's dust covers to see if they contain brake fluid. If so, or if it is obvious that the cylinder(s) have been leaking, replace them or - ONLY if the cylinder bore is in perfect condition - fit a new seal kit.

45. Ensure that the drum brake adjusters (where fitted) are free to rotate (i.e. not seized!). If they are stuck fast, apply a little penetrating oil (but if possible, only from behind the backplate; if you have to work inside the brake drum, take great care to avoid the risk of getting oil on the brake shoes), and gently work the adjuster backwards and forward with a brake adjuster spanner. Eventually the adjusters should free and a little brake grease can be applied to the threads to keep them in this condition. Now rotate the adjuster until the brake shoes contact the drum (preventing the road wheel from turning), then reverse the adjustment just enough to allow the wheel to turn.

46. A similar procedure can be applied to the handbrake adjustment. Check that the handbrake applies the brakes fully, well before it reaches the end of its potential range of movement. Ensure that the handbrake lever remains locked in the 'on' position when fully applied, even if the lever is knocked sideways.

47. Closely check the state of ALL visible hydraulic pipework. If any section of the steel tubing shows signs of corrosion, replace it, for safety as well as to gain an MoT pass. Look too for leakage of fluid around pipe joints, and from the master cylinder. The fluid level in the master cylinder reservoir must also be at its correct level - if not, find out why and rectify the problem! At the front and rear of the vehicle, bend the flexible hydraulic pipes through 180 degrees (by hand) near each end of each pipe, checking for signs of cracking. If any is evident, or if the pipes have been chafing on the tyres, wheels, steering or suspension components, replace them with new items, rerouting them to avoid future problems. Note also that where the manufacturers fitted a clip to secure a piece of pipe, then it must be present and the pipe must be secured by it.

48. Have an assistant press down hard on the brake pedal while you check all flexible pipes for bulges. As an additional check, firmly apply the foot brake and hold the pedal down for a few minutes. It should not slowly sink to the floor (if it does, you have a hydraulic system problem). Press and release the pedal a few times - it should not feel 'spongy' (due to the presence of air in the system). Now check the operation of the brake servo by starting the engine while the brake pedal is being held down. If all is well, as the vacuum servo starts to work, the pedal should move a short distance towards the floor. Check the condition of the servo unit and its hoses - all MUST be sound. If there is the risk of any problems with the braking system's hydraulics, have a qualified mechanic check it over before using the vehicle.

49. A test drive should reveal obvious faults (such as pulling to one side, due to a seized calliper piston, for example), but otherwise all will be revealed on the rollers at the MoT station...

BODYWORK STRUCTURE

A structurally deficient vehicle is a dangerous vehicle, and rust can affect many important areas, including the sills, any 'outriggers' and the floorpan. Examine these areas carefully.

50. Essentially, fractures, cracks or serious corrosion in any load bearing panel or member (to the extent that the affected sections are weakened) need to be dealt with. In addition, failure will result from any deficiencies in the structural metalwork within 30 cm (12 in.) of the seat belt mountings, and also the steering and suspension component attachment points. Repairs made to any structural areas must be carried out by 'continuous' seam welding, and the repair should restore the affected section to at least its original strength.

51. The MoT examiner will be looking for metal which gives way under squeezing pressure between finger and thumb, and will use his wicked little 'Corrosion Assessment Tool' (i.e. a plastic-headed tool known as the 'toffee hammer'!), which in theory at least should be used for detecting rust by lightly tapping the surface. If scraping the surface of the metal shows weakness beneath, the vehicle will fail.

52. Note that the security of doors and other openings must also be assessed, including the hinges, locks and catches. Corrosion damage or other weakness in the vicinity of these items can mean failure. All doors must latch securely. It must be possible to open both front doors from inside and outside the vehicle and rear doors from the outside only.

EXTERIOR BODYWORK

53. Check for another area which can cause problems. Look out for surface rust, or accident damage, on the exterior bodywork, which leaves sharp/jagged edges and which may be liable to cause injury. Ideally, repairs should be carried out by welding in new metal, but for non-structural areas, riveting a plate over a hole, bridging the gap with glass fibre/body filler or even taping over the gap can be legally acceptable, at least as far as the MoT test is concerned.

FUEL SYSTEM

54. Another recent extension of the regulations brings the whole of the fuel system under scrutiny, from the tank to the engine. The system should be examined with and without the engine running, and there must be no leaks from any of the components. The tank must be securely mounted, and the filler cap must fit properly - 'temporary' caps are not permitted.

GETTING THROUGH THE MOT

EMISSIONS

55. Oh dear - even the thought of this aspect can cause headaches. In almost every case, a proper 'engine tune' will help to ensure that your vehicle is running at optimum efficiency, and there should be no difficulty in passing the test, unless your engine, the distributor or the carburettor(s) really are well worn.

All engines are subject to the 'visual smoke emission' test. The engine must be fully warmed up, allowed to idle, then revved slightly. If smoke emitted is regarded by the examiner as being 'excessive', the vehicle will fail. Often smoke emitted during this test is as a result of worn valve stem seals, allowing oil into the combustion chambers during tickover, to be blown out of the exhaust as 'blue smoke' when the engine is revved. In practice, attitudes vary widely between MoT stations on this aspect of the test.

56. For petrol-engined vehicles a 'smoke' test also applies. Again, the engine must be fully warmed up, and allowed to idle, before being revved to around 2,500 Rpm for 20 seconds (to 'purge' the system). If dense blue or black smoke is emitted for more than five seconds, the vehicle will fail. In addition, the exhaust gas is analysed. This result should be within the limits shown in the table here. Please note the lower limits in force from January 1996.

57. A CO reading which is slightly too high can usually be cured by carrying out simple servicing procedures as described in chapter three. It's important to ensure that the fuel is being burnt when and where it should be, which means getting the points, dwell angle, timing and carburation spot-on. However, if the reading is substantially adrift, it points to there being a serious problem and professional help should be sought.

58. Readings on a diesel engine which are too high to pass the test will require the attention of a **SPECIALIST SERVICE**.

PETROL ENGINES

EMISSIONS STANDARDS FROM 1ST JANUARY 1996

PETROL ENGINED VEHICLES WITHOUT CATALYSER
Vehicles first used on or after 10th November 1973
and before 1st October 1986   1200 4.5%
Vehicles first used on or after 1st October 1986   1200 3.5%

PETROL VEHICLES FITTED WITH CATALYTIC CONVERTERS
The new standards will be those specified by the manufacturer at the time of type-approval. The simple emissions test (as above) will be supplemented by a further check to make sure that the catalyst is maintained in good and efficient working order.

DIESEL ENGINES

EMISSIONS STANDARDS FROM 1ST JANUARY 1996
The level of smoke opacity should not exceed 2.5m 3.0m

APPENDIX 1
LUBRICANTS AND
OTHER ESSENTIAL FLUIDS

Castrol has a broad range of top-quality oils, greases and other essential fluids, and they will all figure in the 'Recommended' list appended to the handbooks issued by the major motor manufacturers.

ENGINE OILS

Looking first at the range of engine oils, your only challenge is likely to be in deciding which one is for you - should it be the good old GTX, the choice of home mechanics for many years, or the better and newer GTX2, the GTX3 Lightec, or the Formula RS?

Here's a brief resume of the mineral range:-

GTX3 Lightec (10W/40): Extra highly refined mineral oil, specially formulated for multi-valve, high-technology engines, including turbos, where the manufacturer has recommended light viscosity oil.

GTX2 (15W/40): Designed for newer vehicles, including turbo-charged, where this viscosity is recommended.

GTX (15W/50): The 'superior' multigrade engine oil that is suitable for all vehicles requiring an SAE 15W/50 or 20W/50 viscosity oil, but which is particularly appropriate for older technology engines and high-mileage vehicles, where working clearances have increased over time.

GTD (15W/40): Specially formulated for the particular demands of all diesel engines, including turbo-charged.

Formula RS (10W/60): It's a fully synthetic designed specially for high-output and racing engines....

> **IMPORTANT NOTE:**
> *It is vital for the health of your engine that you only use an oil which is suitable for it. It is essential that you consult your handbook data, or an up-to-date application chart that should be available in your local accessory store. Castrol produce an excellent 'Which Oil?' leaflet available by telephoning 01793 452222 which both details their oils and contains an A-to-Z list of current vehicles together with a note of which of their oils is most suitable for them.*

TRANSMISSION OILS

SYNTRAX UNIVERSAL (75W/90): This advanced technology part-synthetic multi-grade gear oil is available in handy 'squeezy' bottles. It is reckoned to be particularly appropriate for extreme pressure (EP) and high temperature applications, and to suit all gearboxes, transaxles, transfer boxes and final drives requiring a gear oil of SAE 75W, 80W or 90W, or multi-grade formulations within this range.

GREASES

CASTROL LM: A lithium based, high melting point grease that would probably cover most of you needs. It is well proven as a chassis grease (e.g. suspension and steering joints) and is also a good wheel bearing grease for use over a wide range of temperatures. It is suitable for most automotive greasing applications. Other benefits are excellent water resistance and good low temperature 'pumpability'.

CASTROL LMX: Talking of 'pumpability', if you are still into grease gun use, the LMX is the lithium base in a handy cartridge pack that you just load into your grease gun - quick and easy, and none of the mess associated with trying to fill the gun from the can!

CASTROL WATER PUMP GREASE: As its name implies, another one for 'golden oldies' having water pumps fitted with a grease nipple.

CASTROL PH: A lime based grease containing zinc oxide suitable for brake mechanisms and brake shoe pivots - but don't let it contaminate the brake fluid.

CASTROL MOLY: A high melting point lithium base grease containing molybdenum disulphide; suitable for constant velocity (CV) joints where a lithium base grease is specified.

(There is a high performance wheel bearing grease for race and rally use, and also general purpose and specialist trailer and boat application greases).

GENERAL LUBRICATION & FLUIDS

CASTROL EASING FLUID: In aerosol can, it penetrates and releases rusted parts - useful for freeing neglected hinges and other linkages, and for when stripping down old machinery.

CASTROL DWF: Also in aerosol can, this 'de-watering fluid' (DWF) will also penetrate and lubricate as well as displacing and repelling moisture, and it will help to clean and protect all metals.

CASTROL EVERYMAN OIL: Don't let's forget the handy spout-can containing light lubricating oil, although a pump-action oil can (fill it with clean engine oil) is often more useful, particularly where access is awkward.

CASTROL UNIVERSAL BRAKE AND CLUTCH FLUID: A DOT 4 specification synthetic brake (or clutch) fluid suitable for most high performance vehicles not requiring a mineral fluid - e.g. some Jaguar, Rolls Royce and Citroen models (for these Castrol LHM or CHSMO would suit). It can be mixed with all conventional SAE synthetic brake fluids.

CASTROL SUPER DISC: A DOT 5 synthetic brake (or clutch) fluid with superior high performance characteristics, including exceptional anti-vapour lock properties. Best for cars with ABS systems.

CASTROL SRF: A very high performance synthetic brake fluid specially formulated for the race track and other competitive motor sport use.

CASTROL ANTI-FREEZE AND SUMMER COOLANT: Recommended for use in petrol or diesel engine cooling systems, with aluminium or cast iron engines. Its formulation of mono ethylene glycol and corrosion inhibitors makes it suitable for all-year-round use, and because it contains no phosphate it is reckoned that the problems of deposits in some modern uprated engines are eliminated. A 33 per cent concentration will protect down to minus 17 degrees C.

> **ENVIRONMENTAL PROTECTION**
> *"Do not tip oil into any drains. Many drains are connected directly to rivers or streams. Oil can contaminate domestic water sources and kill wildlife. Used oil should be taken to an oil bank for recycling. Telephone the free Oil Bank Line (0800 663366) for your nearest used oil bank"*

APPENDIX 2
AMERICAN AND BRITISH TERMS

It was Mark Twain who described the British and the Americans as, "two nations divided by a common language". such cynicism has no place here but we do acknowledge that our common language evolves in different directions. We hope that this glossary of terms, commonly encountered when servicing your car, will be of assistance to American owners and, in some cases, English speaking owners in other parts of the world, too.

American	British
Antenna	Antenna
Axleshaft	Halfshaft
Back-up	Reverse
Carburetor	Carburettor
Cotter pin	Split pin
Damper	Shock absorber
DC Generator	Dynamo
Defog	Demist
Drive line	Transmission
Driveshaft	Propeller shaft
Fender	Wing or mudguard
Firewall	Bulkhead
First gear	Bottom gear
Float bowl	Float chamber
Freeway, turnpike	Motorway
Frozen	Seized
Gas tank	Petrol tank
Gas pedal	Accelerator or throttle pedal
Gasoline, Gas or Fuel	Petrol or fuel
Ground (electricity)	Earth
Hard top	Fast back
Header	Exhaust manifold
Headlight dimmer	Headlamp dipswitch
High gear	Top gear
Hood	Bonnet
Industrial Alcohol or Denatured Alcohol	Methylated spirit
Kerosene	Paraffin
Lash	Free-play
License plate	Number plate
Lug nut	Wheel nut
Mineral spirit	White spirit
Muffler	Silencer
Oil pan	Sump
Panel wagon/van	Van
Parking light	Side light
Parking brake	Hand brake
'Pinging'	'Pinking'
Quarter window	Quarterlight
Recap (tire)	Remould or retread
Rocker panel	Sill panel

American	British
Rotor or disk (brake)	Disc
Sedan	Saloon
Sheet metal	Bodywork
Shift lever	Gear lever
Side marker lights, side turn signal or position indicator	Side indicator lights
Soft-top	Hood
Spindle arm	Steering arm
Stabiliser or sway bar	Anti-roll bar
Throw-out bearing	Release or thrust bearing
Tie-rod (or connecting rod)	Track rod (or steering)
Tire	Tyre
Transmission	Drive line
Trouble shooting	Fault finding/diagnosis
Trunk	Boot
Turn signal	Indicator
Valve lifter	Tappet
Valve cover	Rocker cover
Valve lifter or tappet	Cam follower or tappet
Vise	Vice
Windshield	Windscreen
Wrench	Spanner

Useful conversions:

	Multiply by
US gallons to Litres	3.785
Litres to US gallons	0.2642
UK gallons to US gallons	1.20095
US gallons to UK gallons	0.832674

Fahrenheit to Celsius (Centigrade) -
Subtract 32, multiply by 0.5555

Celsius to Fahrenheit -
Multiply by 1.8, add 32

APPENDIX 3
SPECIALISTS & SUPPLIERS

All of the products and specialists listed below have contributed in various ways to this book. All of the consumer products used are available through regular high street outlets or by mail order from specialist suppliers.

Autoglym Ltd, Works Road, Letchworth, Herts, SG6 1LM.
Tel: 01462 677766
Bodywork, interior, glass and rubber care and cleaning products.

Automotive Chemicals, Bevis Green Works, Walmersley, Bury, Lancs, BL9 6RE.
Tel: 0161 764 5981
'Car Plan' car care products.

Automotive Products plc, Tachbrook Road, Leamington Spa, Warwicks, CV31 3RE.
Tel: 01926 472251
AP Lockheed and Borg & Beck brakes, clutches, steering and suspension joints, automatic transmissions.

Castrol (UK) Ltd, Burmah House, Pipers Way, Swindon, Wiltshire, SN3 1RE.
Tel: 01793 452222
Contact Castrol's Consumer Technical Department Help Line on the above number for assistance with lubrication recommendations.

Fister (UK) Ltd, Poundmead, Corsham, Wilts, SN13 9NZ.
Tel: 01249 714769
Wiper blades and arms.

Fram Europe Ltd, Llantrisant, Mid Glamorgan, CF7 8YU.
Tel: 01443 223000
Oil, air and fuel filters.

Gunson Ltd, Coppen Road, Dagenham, Essex RM8 1NU
Tel: 0181 984 8855
Electronic tuning aids and carburettor tuning aids including the gas (CO) analysers used throughout this book.

Motaquip, Peugeot Talbot Parts Division, P O Box 126, Torrington Avenue, Tile Hill, Coventry, CV4 9UX.
Tel: 01203 694444
Wide range of service parts, including brake shoes and pads and contact-breaker points.

NGK Spark Plugs (UK) Ltd, 7-8-9 Garrick Industrial Centre, Hendon, London, NW9 6AQ.
Tel: 0181 202 2151
Top quality spark plugs.

Polco-Belcar Ltd, Brent Works, Catherine Wheel Road, Brentford, Middlesex, TW8 8BB.
Tel: 0181 560 6405
Various car accessories and suppliers of the trolley jack used throughout this book.

QH, Quinton Hazell plc, Hazell Way, Bermuda Road, Nuneaton, Warwicks, CV10 7QQ.
Tel: 01203 351010
Huge range of component and service parts, including the 'Moprod' brand.

SP Tools, Sykes-Pickavant Ltd, Kilnhouse Lane, Lytham St. Annes, Lancashire, FY8 3DV.
Tel: 01253 721291
Huge range of specialist and DIY tools and equipment and suppliers of most of the hand tools used in this book.

Unipart Group of Companies, Unipart House, Garsington Road, Cowley, Oxford, OX4 2PG.
Tel: 01865 789966
Huge range of component and service parts, including filters and spark plugs.

W David & Sons Ltd (Isopon), Ridgemount House, 1 Totteridge Lane, Whetstone, London, N20 0EY.
Tel: 0181 445 0372
Manufacturers of the top-quality body repair materials used in this book.

APPENDIX 4
SERVICE HISTORY

This Chapter helps you keep track of all the servicing carried out on your car and can even save you money! A vehicle with a 'service history' is always worth more than one without. Although this book's main purpose is to give invaluable advice to anyone carrying out his or her own servicing, you could make full use of this section, even if you have a garage or mechanic carry out the work for you. It enables you to specify the jobs you want to have carried out to your car and, once again, it enables you to keep that all-important service history. And even if your car doesn't have a 'history' going back to when it was new, keeping this Chapter complete will add to it's value when you come to sell it. Mind you, it obviously won't be enough to just to tick the boxes: keep all your receipts when you buy oil, filters and other consumables or parts. That way, you'll also be able to return any faulty parts if needs be.

IMPORTANT NOTE! The Service Jobs listed here are intended as a check list and a means of keeping a record of your car's service history. It is most important that you refer to **Chapter 5, Service Intervals, Step-by-Step** for full details of how to carry out each Job listed here and for essential SAFETY information, all of which will be essential when you come to carry out the work.

Before carrying out a service, you will need to purchase the right parts. Please refer to **Chapter 2, Buying Spares** for information on how to buy the right parts at the right prices and for the location of your vehicle's 'chassis number'!

Wherever possible, the Jobs listed in this section have been placed in a logical order or placed into groups that will help you make progress quickly. We have tried to save you too much in the way of unnecessary movement by grouping Jobs around areas of the vehicle. Therefore, at each Service Interval, you will see the work grouped into Jobs that need carrying out in the Engine Bay, Around the Car or Under the Car.

You'll also see space at each Service Interval for you to write down the date, price and seller's name every time you buy consumables or accessories. And once again, do remember to *keep your receipts!* There's also space for you to date and sign the Service Record or for a garage's stamp to be applied.

As you move through the Service Intervals, you will notice that the work carried out at, say, *1,500 Miles or Every Month, Whichever Comes First,* is repeated at each one of the following Service Intervals. The same applies to the *6,000 Miles or Six Months* Interval: much of it is repeated at *12,000 Miles or Twelve Months.* Every time a Job or set of Jobs is 'repeated' from an earlier Interval, we show it in a tinted area on the page. You can then see more clearly which jobs are unique to the level of Service Interval that you are on. And you may be surprised to find that all the major Intervals, right up to *36,000 Miles or Thirty Six Months* contain Jobs that are unique to that Service Interval. That's why we have continued this Service History right up to the 3 Year Interval. If you keep your car and wish to continue your service record, you will be able to start the 3 year sequence all over again, in the knowledge that your vehicle has been serviced as well as anyone could wish for!

500 MILES, WEEKLY, OR BEFORE A LONG JOURNEY

This list is shown, complete, only once. It would have been a bit much to have provided the list 52 times over for use once a week throughout the year! They are, however, included with every longer Service list from 3,000 miles/Three Months-on so that each of the 'weekly' jobs is carried out as part of every Service.

500 miles - The Engine Bay

Job 1. Engine oil level.

Job 2. Coolant level.

Job 3. Brake fluid level.

Job 4. Clutch fluid level.

Job 5. Battery electrolyte.

Job 6. Screenwash level.

500 miles - Around the Car

Job 7. Tyre pressures.

Job 8. Check headlamps, rear lights and fuses.

Job 9. Check front indicators.

Job 10. Number plate lights.

Job 11. Reversing and foglamps.

Job 12. Clean lamp lenses.

Job 13. Check horns.

Job 14. Check windscreen wipers.

Job 15. Windscreen washers.

1,500 MILES - OR EVERY MONTH, whichever comes first

These Jobs are similar to the 500 Mile Jobs but don't need carrying out quite so regularly. Once again, these Jobs are not shown with a separate listing for each 1,500/1 Month interval but they are included as part of every 3,000 miles/Three Month Service list and for every longer Service interval.

1,500 miles - Around the Car

Job 16. Check tyres.

Job 17. Check spare tyre.

Job 18. Wash bodywork.

Job 19. Touch-up paintwork.

Job 20. Aerial/antenna.

Job 21. Valet interior.

Job 22. Improve visibility!

1,500 miles - Under the Car

Job 23. Clean mud traps.

3,000 MILES - OR EVERY THREE MONTHS, whichever comes first

All the Service Jobs in the tinted area have been carried forward from earlier service intervals and are to be repeated at this Service.

3,000 miles - The Engine Bay

First carry out all Jobs listed under earlier Service Intervals as applicable.

- [ ] Job 1. Engine oil level.
- [ ] Job 2. Coolant level.
- [ ] Job 3. Brake fluid level.
- [ ] Job 4. Clutch fluid level.
- [ ] Job 5. Battery electrolyte.
- [ ] Job 6. Screenwash level.

- [ ] Job 24. Generator drive belt.
- [ ] Job 25. Carb dashpots.
- [ ] Job 26. Check brake/fuel lines.

3,000 miles - Around the Car

First carry out all Jobs listed under earlier Service Intervals as applicable.

- [ ] Job 7. Tyre pressures.
- [ ] Job 8. Check headlamps, rear lights and fuses.
- [ ] Job 9. Check front indicators.
- [ ] Job 10. Number plate lights.
- [ ] Job 11. Reversing and foglamps.
- [ ] Job 12. Clean lamp lenses.
- [ ] Job 13. Check horns.
- [ ] Job 14. Check windscreen wipers.
- [ ] Job 15. Windscreen washers.
- [ ] Job 16. Check tyres.
- [ ] Job 17. Check spare tyre.
- [ ] Job 18. Wash bodywork.
- [ ] Job 19. Touch-up paintwork.
- [ ] Job 20. Aerial/antenna.
- [ ] Job 21. Valet interior.
- [ ] Job 22. Improve visibility!

☐ Job 27. Pipes and hoses.

☐ Job 28. Check handbrake adjustment.

☐ Job 29. Door and tailgate seals.

☐ Job 30. Check windscreen.

☐ Job 31. Rear view mirrors.

☐ Job 32. Wash and wax the bodywork.

3,000 miles - Under the Car

First carry out all Jobs listed under earlier Service Intervals as applicable.

☐ Job 23. Clean mud traps.

☐ Job 33. Check exhaust system.

☐ Job 34. Check steering rack gaiters.

☐ Job 35. Track rod ends.

☐ Job 36. Check drive-shaft gaiters.

☐ Job 37. Grease points.

☐ Job 38. Inspect for leaks.

3,000 miles - Road Test

☐ Job 39. Clean controls.

☐ Job 40. Check instruments.

☐ Job 41. Throttle pedal.

☐ Job 42. Handbrake function.

☐ Job 43. Brakes and steering.

Date serviced:....................................

Carried out by: ....
Garage Stamp or signature:

Parts/Accessories purchased (date, parts,

source) ....

....

....

....

....

....

6,000 MILES - OR EVERY SIX MONTHS, whichever comes first

All the Service Jobs in the tinted area have been carried forward from earlier service intervals and are to be repeated at this Service.

6,000 miles - The Engine Bay

First carry out all Jobs listed under earlier Service Intervals as applicable.

☐ Job 1. Engine oil level.

☐ Job 2. Coolant level.

☐ Job 3. Brake fluid level.

☐ Job 4. Clutch fluid level.

☐ Job 5. Battery electrolyte.

☐ Job 6. Screenwash level.

☐ Job 24. Generator drive belt.

☐ Job 25. Carb dashpots.

☐ Job 26. Check brake/fuel lines.

6,000 miles - Under the Car

First carry out all Jobs listed under earlier Service Intervals as applicable.

☐ Job 23. Clean mud traps.

☐ Job 33. Check exhaust system.

☐ Job 34. Check steering rack gaiters.

☐ Job 35. Track rod ends.

☐ Job 36. Check drive-shaft gaiters.

☐ Job 37. Grease points.

☐ Job 38. Inspect for leaks.

☐ Job 44. Change engine oil/oil filter.

☐ Job 45. Renew oil filter.

☐ Job 46. Spark plugs.

☐ Job 47. Distributor.

☐ Job 48. Ignition timing.

☐ Job 49. Accelerator controls.

☐ Job 50. Carburettor settings.

☐ Job 51. Check clutch adjustment.

☐ Job 52. Cooling system.

☐ Job 53. Coolant check.

☐ Job 54. Heater controls.

☐ Job 55. Check water pump.

☐ Job 56. Check automatic transmission fluid.

☐ Job 57. Check power steering fluid.

6,000 miles - Around the Car

First carry out all Jobs listed under earlier Service Intervals as applicable.

☐ Job 7. Tyre pressures.

☐ Job 8. Check headlamps, rear lights and fuses.

☐ Job 9. Check front indicators.

☐ Job 10. Number plate lights.

☐ Job 11. Reversing and foglamps.

☐ Job 12. Clean lamp lenses.

☐ Job 13. Check horns.

☐ Job 14. Check windscreen wipers.

☐ Job 15. Windscreen washers.

☐ Job 16. Check tyres.

☐ Job 17. Check spare tyre.

☐ Job 18. Wash bodywork.

☐ Job 19. Touch-up paintwork.

☐ Job 20. Aerial/antenna.

☐ Job 21. Valet interior.

☐ Job 22. Improve visibility!

☐ Job 27. Pipes and hoses.

☐ Job 28. Check handbrake adjustment.

☐ Job 29. Door and tailgate seals.

☐ Job 30. Check windscreen.

☐ Job 31. Rear view mirrors.

☐ Job 32. Wash and wax the bodywork.

☐ Job 58. Check seat belts.

☐ Job 59. Renew wiper blades.

☐ Job 60. Locks and hinges.

☐ Job 61. Cable release mechanisms.

☐ Job 62. Check seats & seat belts.

☐ Job 63. Test Dampers.

☐ Job 64. Check/renew disc brake pads.

☐ Job 65. Check/adjust drum brakes shoes.

9,000 MILES - OR EVERY NINE MONTHS, whichever comes first.

All the Service Jobs at this Service Interval have been carried forward from earlier service intervals and are to be repeated at this Service.

9,000 miles - The Engine Bay

First carry out all Jobs listed under earlier Service Intervals as applicable.

☐ Job 1. Engine oil level.

☐ Job 2. Coolant level.

☐ Job 3. Brake fluid level.

☐ Job 4. Clutch fluid level.

☐ Job 5. Battery electrolyte.

☐ Job 6. Screenwash level.

☐ Job 24. Generator drive belt.

☐ Job 25. Carb dashpots.

☐ Job 26. Check brake/fuel lines.

9,000 miles - Around the Car

First carry out all Jobs listed under earlier Service Intervals as applicable.

☐ Job 7. Tyre pressures.

☐ Job 8. Check headlamps, rear lights and fuses.

☐ Job 9. Check front indicators.

☐ Job 10. Number plate lights.

☐ Job 11. Reversing and foglamps.

☐ Job 12. Clean lamp lenses.

☐ Job 13. Check horns.

☐ Job 14. Check windscreen wipers.

☐ Job 15. Windscreen washers.

☐ Job 16. Check tyres.

☐ Job 17. Check spare tyre.

☐ Job 18. Wash bodywork.

☐ Job 19. Touch-up paintwork.

☐ Job 20. Aerial/antenna.

☐ Job 21. Valet interior.

☐ Job 22. Improve visibility!

☐ Job 27. Pipes and hoses.

☐ Job 28. Check handbrake adjustment.

Date serviced:...

Carried out by:...
Garage Stamp or signature:

Parts/Accessories purchased (date, parts, source) ....

....

....

....

....

....

- [ ] Job 29. Door and tailgate seals.
- [ ] Job 30. Check windscreen.
- [ ] Job 31. Rear view mirrors.
- [ ] Job 32. Wash and wax the bodywork.

9,000 miles - Under the Car

First carry out all Jobs listed under earlier Service Intervals as applicable.

- [ ] Job 23. Clean mud traps.
- [ ] Job 33. Check exhaust system.
- [ ] Job 34. Check steering rack gaiters.
- [ ] Job 35. Track rod ends.
- [ ] Job 36. Check drive-shaft gaiters.
- [ ] Job 37. Grease points.
- [ ] Job 38. Inspect for leaks.

9,000 miles - Road Test

First carry out all Jobs listed under earlier Service Intervals as applicable.

- [ ] Job 39. Clean controls.
- [ ] Job 40. Check instruments.
- [ ] Job 41. Throttle pedal.
- [ ] Job 42. Handbrake function.
- [ ] Job 43. Brakes and steering.

Date serviced:...

Carried out by: ....
Garage Stamp or signature:

Parts/Accessories purchased (date, parts,

source) ....

....

....

....

....

12,000 MILES - OR EVERY TWELVE MONTHS, whichever comes first

All the Service Jobs in the tinted area have been carried forward from earlier service intervals and are to be repeated at this Service.

12,000 miles - The Engine Bay

First carry out all Jobs listed under earlier Service Intervals as applicable.

- [ ] Job 1. Engine oil level.
- [ ] Job 2. Coolant level.
- [ ] Job 3. Brake fluid level.
- [ ] Job 4. Clutch fluid level.
- [ ] Job 5. Battery electrolyte.
- [ ] Job 6. Screenwash level.
- [ ] Job 24. Generator drive belt.
- [ ] Job 25. Carb dashpots.
- [ ] Job 26. Check brake/fuel lines.

- [ ] Job 66. Check valve clearances.
- [ ] Job 67. Rocker cover gasket.
- [ ] Job 68. Positive crankcase breather.
- [ ] Job 69. Air cleaner element.
- [ ] Job 70. Air cleaner intake adjustment.
- [ ] Job 71. Check/renew fuel filter.
- [ ] Job 72. Check coolant hoses.
- [ ] Job 73. Anti-freeze.
- [ ] Job 74. Battery terminals.
- [ ] Job 75. Brake servo filter.

12,000 miles - Around the Car

First carry out all Jobs listed under earlier Service Intervals as applicable.

- [ ] Job 7. Tyre pressures.
- [ ] Job 8. Check headlamps, rear lights and fuses.
- [ ] Job 9. Check front indicators.
- [ ] Job 10. Number plate lights.
- [ ] Job 11. Reversing and foglamps.
- [ ] Job 12. Clean lamp lenses.
- [ ] Job 13. Check horns.
- [ ] Job 14. Check windscreen wipers.
- [ ] Job 15. Windscreen washers.
- [ ] Job 16. Check tyres.
- [ ] Job 17. Check spare tyre.
- [ ] Job 18. Wash bodywork.
- [ ] Job 19. Touch-up paintwork.
- [ ] Job 20. Aerial/antenna.
- [ ] Job 21. Valet interior.
- [ ] Job 22. Improve visibility!
- [ ] Job 27. Pipes and hoses.
- [ ] Job 28. Check handbrake adjustment.
- [ ] Job 29. Door and tailgate seals.
- [ ] Job 30. Check windscreen.
- [ ] Job 31. Rear view mirrors.
- [ ] Job 32. Wash and wax the bodywork.
- [ ] Job 58. Check seat belts.
- [ ] Job 59. Renew wiper blades.
- [ ] Job 60. Locks and hinges.
- [ ] Job 61. Cable release mechanisms.
- [ ] Job 62. Check seats & seat belts.
- [ ] Job 63. Test Dampers.
- [ ] Job 64. Check/renew disc brake pads.
- [ ] Job 65. Check/adjust drum brakes shoes.

- [ ] Job 76. Toolkit and jack.
- [ ] Job 77. Lamp seals.
- [ ] Job 78. Alarm remote units.
- [ ] Job 79. Adjust headlights.
- [ ] Job 80. Check hub bearings.
- [ ] Job 81. Check steering and suspension.
- [ ] Job 82. Exhaust emissions.

12,000 miles - Under the Car

First carry out all Jobs listed under earlier Service Intervals as applicable.

- [ ] Job 23. Clean mud traps.
- [ ] Job 33. Check exhaust system.
- [ ] Job 34. Check steering rack gaiters.
- [ ] Job 35. Track rod ends.
- [ ] Job 36. Check drive-shaft gaiters.
- [ ] Job 37. Grease points.
- [ ] Job 38. Inspect for leaks.
- [ ] Job 44. Change engine oil/oil filter.
- [ ] Job 45. Renew oil filter.
- [ ] Job 46. Spark plugs.
- [ ] Job 47. Distributor.
- [ ] Job 48. Ignition timing.
- [ ] Job 49. Accelerator controls.
- [ ] Job 50. Carburettor settings.
- [ ] Job 51. Check clutch adjustment.
- [ ] Job 52. Cooling system.
- [ ] Job 53. Coolant check.
- [ ] Job 54. Heater controls.
- [ ] Job 55. Check water pump.
- [ ] Job 56. Check automatic transmission fluid.
- [ ] Job 57. Check power steering fluid.

- [ ] Job 83. Inspect underside.
- [ ] Job 84. Clear drain holes.
- [ ] Job 85. Check gearbox oil.
- [ ] Job 86. Check rear axle oil.
- [ ] Job 87. Check transaxle oil.
- [ ] Job 88. Check telescopic dampers.
- [ ] Job 89. Check lever-arm dampers.
- [ ] Job 90. Clutch hydraulics.

Date serviced:...

Carried out by:...
Garage Stamp or signature:

Parts/Accessories purchased (date, parts, source) ....

15,000 MILES - OR EVERY FIFTEEN MONTHS, whichever comes first

All the Service Jobs at this Service interval have been carried forward from earlier service intervals and are to be repeated at this Service.

15,000 miles - The Engine Bay

First carry out all Jobs listed under earlier Service Intervals as applicable.

- [ ] Job 1. Engine oil level.
- [ ] Job 2. Coolant level.
- [ ] Job 3. Brake fluid level.
- [ ] Job 4. Clutch fluid level.
- [ ] Job 5. Battery electrolyte.
- [ ] Job 6. Screenwash level.
- [ ] Job 24. Generator drive belt.
- [ ] Job 25. Carb dashpots.
- [ ] Job 26. Check brake/fuel lines.

15,000 miles - Around the Car

First carry out all Jobs listed under earlier Service Intervals as applicable.

- [ ] Job 7. Tyre pressures.
- [ ] Job 8. Check headlamps, rear lights and fuses.
- [ ] Job 9. Check front indicators.
- [ ] Job 10. Number plate lights.
- [ ] Job 11. Reversing and foglamps.
- [ ] Job 12. Clean lamp lenses.
- [ ] Job 13. Check horns.
- [ ] Job 14. Check windscreen wipers.
- [ ] Job 15. Windscreen washers.
- [ ] Job 16. Check tyres.
- [ ] Job 17. Check spare tyre.
- [ ] Job 18. Wash bodywork.
- [ ] Job 19. Touch-up paintwork.
- [ ] Job 20. Aerial/antenna.
- [ ] Job 21. Valet interior.
- [ ] Job 22. Improve visibility!
- [ ] Job 27. Pipes and hoses.
- [ ] Job 28. Check handbrake adjustment.

- [ ] Job 29. Door and tailgate seals.
- [ ] Job 30. Check windscreen.
- [ ] Job 31. Rear view mirrors.
- [ ] Job 32. Wash and wax the bodywork.

15000 miles - Under the Car

First carry out all Jobs listed under earlier Service Intervals as applicable.

- [ ] Job 23. Clean mud traps.
- [ ] Job 33. Check exhaust system.
- [ ] Job 34. Check steering rack gaiters.
- [ ] Job 35. Track rod ends.
- [ ] Job 36. Check drive-shaft gaiters.
- [ ] Job 37. Grease points.
- [ ] Job 38. Inspect for leaks.

15,000 miles - Road Test

First carry out all Jobs listed under earlier Service Intervals as applicable.

- [ ] Job 39. Clean controls.
- [ ] Job 40. Check instruments.
- [ ] Job 41. Throttle pedal.
- [ ] Job 42. Handbrake function.
- [ ] Job 43. Brakes and steering.

18,000 MILES - OR EVERY EIGHTEEN MONTHS, whichever comes first

All the Service Jobs in the tinted area have been carried forward from earlier service intervals and are to be repeated at this Service.

18,000 miles - The Engine Bay

First carry out all Jobs listed under earlier Service Intervals as applicable.

- [ ] Job 1. Engine oil level.
- [ ] Job 2. Coolant level.
- [ ] Job 3. Brake fluid level.
- [ ] Job 4. Clutch fluid level.
- [ ] Job 5. Battery electrolyte.
- [ ] Job 6. Screenwash level.
- [ ] Job 24. Generator drive belt.
- [ ] Job 25. Carb dashpots.
- [ ] Job 26. Check brake/fuel lines.

18,000 miles - Under the Car

First carry out all Jobs listed under earlier Service Intervals as applicable.

- [ ] Job 23. Clean mud traps.
- [ ] Job 33. Check exhaust system.
- [ ] Job 34. Check steering rack gaiters.
- [ ] Job 35. Track rod ends.
- [ ] Job 36. Check drive-shaft gaiters.
- [ ] Job 37. Grease points.
- [ ] Job 38. Inspect for leaks.
- [ ] Job 44. Change engine oil/oil filter.
- [ ] Job 45. Renew oil filter.
- [ ] Job 46. Spark plugs.
- [ ] Job 47. Distributor.
- [ ] Job 48. Ignition timing.
- [ ] Job 49. Accelerator controls.
- [ ] Job 50. Carburettor settings.
- [ ] Job 51. Check clutch adjustment.
- [ ] Job 52. Cooling system.
- [ ] Job 53. Coolant check.
- [ ] Job 54. Heater controls.
- [ ] Job 55. Check water pump.
- [ ] Job 56. Check automatic transmission fluid.
- [ ] Job 57. Check power steering fluid.

Date serviced:..

Carried out by:...
Garage Stamp or signature:

Parts/Accessories purchased (date, parts,

source) ....

....

....

....

....

18,000 miles - Around the Car

First carry out all Jobs listed under earlier Service Intervals as applicable.

- [ ] Job 7. Tyre pressures.
- [ ] Job 8. Check headlamps, rear lights and fuses.
- [ ] Job 9. Check front indicators.
- [ ] Job 10. Number plate lights.
- [ ] Job 11. Reversing and foglamps.
- [ ] Job 12. Clean lamp lenses.
- [ ] Job 13. Check horns.
- [ ] Job 14. Check windscreen wipers.
- [ ] Job 15. Windscreen washers.
- [ ] Job 16. Check tyres.
- [ ] Job 17. Check spare tyre.
- [ ] Job 18. Wash bodywork.
- [ ] Job 19. Touch-up paintwork.
- [ ] Job 20. Aerial/antenna.
- [ ] Job 21. Valet interior.
- [ ] Job 22. Improve visibility!
- [ ] Job 27. Pipes and hoses.
- [ ] Job 28. Check handbrake adjustment.
- [ ] Job 29. Door and tailgate seals.
- [ ] Job 30. Check windscreen.
- [ ] Job 31. Rear view mirrors.
- [ ] Job 32. Wash and wax the bodywork.
- [ ] Job 58. Check seat belts.
- [ ] Job 59. Renew wiper blades.
- [ ] Job 60. Locks and hinges.
- [ ] Job 61. Cable release mechanisms.
- [ ] Job 62. Check seats & seat belts.
- [ ] Job 63. Test Dampers.
- [ ] Job 64. Check/renew disc brake pads.
- [ ] Job 65. Check/adjust drum brakes shoes.

Date serviced: ....

Carried out by: ....
Garage Stamp or signature:

Parts/Accessories purchased (date, parts,

source) ....

....

....

....

....

....

21,000 MILES - OR EVERY TWENTY ONE MONTHS, whichever comes first.

All the Service Jobs at this Service Interval have been carried forward from earlier service intervals and are to be repeated at this Service.

21,000 miles - The Engine Bay

First carry out all Jobs listed under earlier Service Intervals as applicable.

- [ ] Job 1. Engine oil level.
- [ ] Job 2. Coolant level.
- [ ] Job 3. Brake fluid level.
- [ ] Job 4. Clutch fluid level.
- [ ] Job 5. Battery electrolyte.
- [ ] Job 6. Screenwash level.
- [ ] Job 24. Generator drive belt.
- [ ] Job 25. Carb dashpots.
- [ ] Job 26. Check brake/fuel lines.

21,000 miles - Around the Car

First carry out all Jobs listed under earlier Service Intervals as applicable.

- [ ] Job 7. Tyre pressures.
- [ ] Job 8. Check headlamps, rear lights and fuses.
- [ ] Job 9. Check front indicators.
- [ ] Job 10. Number plate lights.
- [ ] Job 11. Reversing and foglamps.
- [ ] Job 12. Clean lamp lenses.
- [ ] Job 13. Check horns.
- [ ] Job 14. Check windscreen wipers.
- [ ] Job 15. Windscreen washers.
- [ ] Job 16. Check tyres.
- [ ] Job 17. Check spare tyre.
- [ ] Job 18. Wash bodywork.
- [ ] Job 19. Touch-up paintwork.
- [ ] Job 20. Aerial/antenna.
- [ ] Job 21. Valet interior.
- [ ] Job 22. Improve visibility!
- [ ] Job 27. Pipes and hoses.
- [ ] Job 28. Check handbrake adjustment.

☐ Job 29. Door and tailgate seals.

☐ Job 30. Check windscreen.

☐ Job 31. Rear view mirrors.

☐ Job 32. Wash and wax the bodywork.

21,000 miles - Under the Car

First carry out all Jobs listed under earlier Service Intervals as applicable.

☐ Job 23. Clean mud traps.

☐ Job 33. Check exhaust system.

☐ Job 34. Check steering rack gaiters.

☐ Job 35. Track rod ends.

☐ Job 36. Check drive-shaft gaiters.

☐ Job 37. Grease points.

☐ Job 38. Inspect for leaks.

21,000 miles - Road Test

First carry out all Jobs listed under earlier Service Intervals as applicable.

☐ Job 39. Clean controls.

☐ Job 40. Check instruments.

☐ Job 41. Throttle pedal.

☐ Job 42. Handbrake function.

☐ Job 43. Brakes and steering.

Date serviced:...

Carried out by: ....
Garage Stamp or signature:

Parts/Accessories purchased (date, parts,

source) ....

....

....

....

....

24,000 MILES - OR EVERY TWENTY FOUR MONTHS, whichever comes first.

All the Service Jobs in the tinted area have been carried forward from earlier service intervals and are to be repeated at this Service.

24,000 mile - The Engine Bay

First carry out all Jobs listed under earlier Service Intervals as applicable.

☐ Job 1. Engine oil level.

☐ Job 2. Coolant level.

☐ Job 3. Brake fluid level.

☐ Job 4. Clutch fluid level.

☐ Job 5. Battery electrolyte.

☐ Job 6. Screenwash level.

☐ Job 24. Generator drive belt.

☐ Job 25. Carb dashpots.

☐ Job 26. Check brake/fuel lines.

☐ Job 66. Check valve clearances.

☐ Job 67. Rocker cover gasket.

☐ Job 68. Positive crankcase breather.

☐ Job 69. Air cleaner element.

☐ Job 70. Air cleaner intake adjustment.

☐ Job 71. Check/renew fuel filter.

☐ Job 72. Check coolant hoses.

☐ Job 73. Anti-freeze.

☐ Job 74. Battery terminals.

☐ Job 75. Brake servo filter.

☐ Job 91. Radiator pressure cap.

☐ Job 92. Refill cooling system.

☐ Job 93. Check brake discs.

☐ Job 94. Brake callipers.

☐ Job 95. Renew brake fluid.

☐ Job 96. Check brake drums.

24,000 miles - Around the Car

First carry out all Jobs listed under earlier Service Intervals as applicable.

☐ Job 7. Tyre pressures.

☐ Job 8. Check headlamps, rear lights and fuses.

☐ Job 9. Check front indicators.

☐ Job 10. Number plate lights.

☐ Job 11. Reversing and foglamps.

☐ Job 12. Clean lamp lenses.

☐ Job 13. Check horns.

☐ Job 14. Check windscreen wipers.

☐ Job 15. Windscreen washers.

☐ Job 16. Check tyres.

☐ Job 17. Check spare tyre.

☐ Job 18. Wash bodywork.

☐ Job 19. Touch-up paintwork.

☐ Job 20. Aerial/antenna.

☐ Job 21. Valet interior.

☐ Job 22. Improve visibility!

☐ Job 27. Pipes and hoses.

☐ Job 28. Check handbrake adjustment.

☐ Job 29. Door and tailgate seals.

☐ Job 30. Check windscreen.

☐ Job 31. Rear view mirrors.

☐ Job 32. Wash and wax the bodywork.

☐ Job 58. Check seat belts.

☐ Job 59. Renew wiper blades.

☐ Job 60. Locks and hinges.

☐ Job 61. Cable release mechanisms.

☐ Job 62. Check seats & seat belts.

☐ Job 63. Test Dampers.

☐ Job 64. Check/renew disc brake pads.

☐ Job 65. Check/adjust drum brakes shoes.

☐ Job 76. Toolkit and jack.

☐ Job 77. Lamp seals.

☐ Job 78. Alarm remote units.

☐ Job 79. Adjust headlights.

☐ Job 80. Check hub bearings.

☐ Job 81. Check steering and suspension.

☐ Job 82. Exhaust emissions.

24,000 miles - Under the Car

First carry out all Jobs listed under earlier Service Intervals as applicable.

- [ ] Job 23. Clean mud traps.
- [ ] Job 33. Check exhaust system.
- [ ] Job 34. Check steering rack gaiters.
- [ ] Job 35. Track rod ends.
- [ ] Job 36. Check drive-shaft gaiters.
- [ ] Job 37. Grease points.
- [ ] Job 38. Inspect for leaks.
- [ ] Job 44. Change engine oil/oil filter.
- [ ] Job 45. Renew oil filter.
- [ ] Job 46. Spark plugs.
- [ ] Job 47. Distributor.
- [ ] Job 48. Ignition timing.
- [ ] Job 49. Accelerator controls.
- [ ] Job 50. Carburettor settings.
- [ ] Job 51. Check clutch adjustment.
- [ ] Job 52. Cooling system.
- [ ] Job 53. Coolant check.
- [ ] Job 54. Heater controls.
- [ ] Job 55. Check water pump.
- [ ] Job 56. Check automatic transmission fluid.
- [ ] Job 57. Check power steering fluid.
- [ ] Job 83. Inspect underside.
- [ ] Job 84. Clear drain holes.
- [ ] Job 85. Check gearbox oil.
- [ ] Job 86. Check rear axle oil.
- [ ] Job 87. Check transaxle oil.
- [ ] Job 88. Check telescopic dampers.
- [ ] Job 89. Check lever-arm dampers.
- [ ] Job 90. Clutch hydraulics.

Date serviced:...

Carried out by:...
Garage Stamp or signature:

Parts/Accessories purchased (date, parts,

source) ....

....

....

....

....

....

27,000 MILES - OR EVERY TWENTY SEVEN MONTHS, whichever comes first.

All the Service Jobs at this Service Interval have been carried forward from earlier service intervals and are to be carried out at this Service.

27,000 miles - The Engine Bay

First carry out all Jobs listed under earlier Service Intervals as applicable.

- [ ] Job 1. Engine oil level.
- [ ] Job 2. Coolant level.
- [ ] Job 3. Brake fluid level.
- [ ] Job 4. Clutch fluid level.
- [ ] Job 5. Battery electrolyte.
- [ ] Job 6. Screenwash level.
- [ ] Job 24. Generator drive belt.
- [ ] Job 25. Carb dashpots.
- [ ] Job 26. Check brake/fuel lines.

27,000 miles - Around the Car

First carry out all Jobs listed under earlier Service Intervals as applicable.

- [ ] Job 7. Tyre pressures.
- [ ] Job 8. Check headlamps, rear lights and fuses.
- [ ] Job 9. Check front indicators.
- [ ] Job 10. Number plate lights.
- [ ] Job 11. Reversing and foglamps.
- [ ] Job 12. Clean lamp lenses.
- [ ] Job 13. Check horns.
- [ ] Job 14. Check windscreen wipers.
- [ ] Job 15. Windscreen washers.
- [ ] Job 16. Check tyres.
- [ ] Job 17. Check spare tyre.
- [ ] Job 18. Wash bodywork.
- [ ] Job 19. Touch-up paintwork.
- [ ] Job 20. Aerial/antenna.
- [ ] Job 21. Valet interior.
- [ ] Job 22. Improve visibility!
- [ ] Job 27. Pipes and hoses.
- [ ] Job 28. Check handbrake adjustment.

☐ Job 29. Door and tailgate seals.

☐ Job 30. Check windscreen.

☐ Job 31. Rear view mirrors.

☐ Job 32. Wash and wax the bodywork.

27,000 miles - Under the Car

First carry out all Jobs listed under earlier Service Intervals as applicable.

☐ Job 23. Clean mud traps.

☐ Job 33. Check exhaust system.

☐ Job 34. Check steering rack gaiters.

☐ Job 35. Track rod ends.

☐ Job 36. Check drive-shaft gaiters.

☐ Job 37. Grease points.

☐ Job 38. Inspect for leaks.

27,000 miles - Road Test

First carry out all Jobs listed under earlier Service Intervals as applicable.

☐ Job 39. Clean controls.

☐ Job 40. Check instruments.

☐ Job 41. Throttle pedal.

☐ Job 42. Handbrake function.

☐ Job 43. Brakes and steering.

30,000 MILES - OR EVERY THIRTY MONTHS, whichever comes first.

All the Service Jobs at this Service Interval have been carried forward from earlier service intervals and are to be repeated at this Service.

30,000 miles - The Engine Bay

First carry out all Jobs listed under earlier Service Intervals as applicable.

☐ Job 1. Engine oil level.

☐ Job 2. Coolant level.

☐ Job 3. Brake fluid level.

☐ Job 4. Clutch fluid level.

☐ Job 5. Battery electrolyte.

☐ Job 6. Screenwash level.

☐ Job 24. Generator drive belt.

☐ Job 25. Carb dashpots.

☐ Job 26. Check brake/fuel lines.

30,000 miles - Under the Car

First carry out all Jobs listed under earlier Service Intervals as applicable.

☐ Job 23. Clean mud traps.

☐ Job 33. Check exhaust system.

☐ Job 34. Check steering rack gaiters.

☐ Job 35. Track rod ends.

☐ Job 36. Check drive-shaft gaiters.

☐ Job 37. Grease points.

☐ Job 38. Inspect for leaks.

☐ Job 44. Change engine oil/oil filter.

☐ Job 45. Renew oil filter.

☐ Job 46. Spark plugs.

☐ Job 47. Distributor.

☐ Job 48. Ignition timing.

☐ Job 49. Accelerator controls.

☐ Job 50. Carburettor settings.

☐ Job 51. Check clutch adjustment.

☐ Job 52. Cooling system.

☐ Job 53. Coolant check.

☐ Job 54. Heater controls.

☐ Job 55. Check water pump.

☐ Job 56. Check automatic transmission fluid.

☐ Job 57. Check power steering fluid.

Date serviced:..

Carried out by: ....
Garage Stamp or signature:

Parts/Accessories purchased (date, parts,

source) ....

....

....

....

....

30,000 miles - Around the Car

First carry out all Jobs listed under earlier Service Intervals as applicable.

☐ Job 7. Tyre pressures.

☐ Job 8. Check headlamps, rear lights and fuses.

☐ Job 9. Check front indicators.

☐ Job 10. Number plate lights.

☐ Job 11. Reversing and foglamps.

☐ Job 12. Clean lamp lenses.

☐ Job 13. Check horns.

☐ Job 14. Check windscreen wipers.

☐ Job 15. Windscreen washers.

☐ Job 16. Check tyres.

☐ Job 17. Check spare tyre.

☐ Job 18. Wash bodywork.

☐ Job 19. Touch-up paintwork.

☐ Job 20. Aerial/antenna.

☐ Job 21. Valet interior.

☐ Job 22. Improve visibility!

☐ Job 27. Pipes and hoses.

☐ Job 28. Check handbrake adjustment.

☐ Job 29. Door and tailgate seals.

☐ Job 30. Check windscreen.

☐ Job 31. Rear view mirrors.

☐ Job 32. Wash and wax the bodywork.

☐ Job 58. Check seat belts.

☐ Job 59. Renew wiper blades.

☐ Job 60. Locks and hinges.

☐ Job 61. Cable release mechanisms.

☐ Job 62. Check seats & seat belts.

☐ Job 63. Test Dampers.

☐ Job 64. Check/renew disc brake pads.

☐ Job 65. Check/adjust drum brakes shoes.

Date serviced:...

Carried out by:...
Garage Stamp or signature:

Parts/Accessories purchased (date, parts,

source)..

....

....

....

....

....

33,000 MILES - OR EVERY THIRTY THREE MONTHS, whichever comes first.

All the Service Jobs at this Service Interval have been carried forward from earlier service intervals and are to be repeated at this Service.

33,000 miles - The Engine Bay

First carry out all Jobs listed under earlier Service Intervals as applicable.

☐ Job 1. Engine oil level.

☐ Job 2. Coolant level.

☐ Job 3. Brake fluid level.

☐ Job 4. Clutch fluid level.

☐ Job 5. Battery electrolyte.

☐ Job 6. Screenwash level.

☐ Job 24. Generator drive belt.

☐ Job 25. Carb dashpots.

☐ Job 26. Check brake/fuel lines.

33,000 miles - Around the Car

First carry out all Jobs listed under earlier Service Intervals as applicable.

☐ Job 7. Tyre pressures.

☐ Job 8. Check headlamps, rear lights and fuses.

☐ Job 9. Check front indicators.

☐ Job 10. Number plate lights.

☐ Job 11. Reversing and foglamps.

☐ Job 12. Clean lamp lenses.

☐ Job 13. Check horns.

☐ Job 14. Check windscreen wipers.

☐ Job 15. Windscreen washers.

☐ Job 16. Check tyres.

☐ Job 17. Check spare tyre.

☐ Job 18. Wash bodywork.

☐ Job 19. Touch-up paintwork.

☐ Job 20. Aerial/antenna.

☐ Job 21. Valet interior.

☐ Job 22. Improve visibility!

☐ Job 27. Pipes and hoses.

☐ Job 28. Check handbrake adjustment.

- [ ] Job 29. Door and tailgate seals.
- [ ] Job 30. Check windscreen.
- [ ] Job 31. Rear view mirrors.
- [ ] Job 32. Wash and wax the bodywork.

33,000 miles - Under the Car

First carry out all Jobs listed under earlier Service Intervals as applicable.

- [ ] Job 23. Clean mud traps.
- [ ] Job 33. Check exhaust system.
- [ ] Job 34. Check steering rack gaiters.
- [ ] Job 35. Track rod ends.
- [ ] Job 36. Check drive-shaft gaiters.
- [ ] Job 37. Grease points.
- [ ] Job 38. Inspect for leaks.

33,000 miles - Road Test

First carry out all Jobs listed under earlier Service Intervals as applicable.

- [ ] Job 39. Clean controls.
- [ ] Job 40. Check instruments.
- [ ] Job 41. Throttle pedal.
- [ ] Job 42. Handbrake function.
- [ ] Job 43. Brakes and steering.

Date serviced:...

Carried out by: ....
Garage Stamp or signature:

Parts/Accessories purchased (date, parts,

source) ....

....

....

....

....

36,000 MILES - OR EVERY THIRTY SIX MONTHS, whichever comes first.

All the Service Jobs in the tinted area have been carried forward from earlier service intervals and are to be repeated at this Service.

36,000 miles - The Engine Bay

First carry out all Jobs listed under earlier Service Intervals as applicable.

- [ ] Job 1. Engine oil level.
- [ ] Job 2. Coolant level.
- [ ] Job 3. Brake fluid level.
- [ ] Job 4. Clutch fluid level.
- [ ] Job 5. Battery electrolyte.
- [ ] Job 6. Screenwash level.
- [ ] Job 24. Generator drive belt.
- [ ] Job 25. Carb dashpots.
- [ ] Job 26. Check brake/fuel lines.
- [ ] Job 66. Check valve clearances.
- [ ] Job 67. Rocker cover gasket.
- [ ] Job 68. Positive crankcase breather.
- [ ] Job 69. Air cleaner element.
- [ ] Job 70. Air cleaner intake adjustment.
- [ ] Job 71. Check/renew fuel filter.
- [ ] Job 72. Check coolant hoses.
- [ ] Job 73. Anti-freeze.
- [ ] Job 74. Battery terminals.
- [ ] Job 75. Brake servo filter.

- [ ] Job 97. Renew camshaft belt.

36,000 miles - Around the Car

First carry out all Jobs listed under earlier Service Intervals as applicable.

- [ ] Job 7. Tyre pressures.
- [ ] Job 8. Check headlamps, rear lights and fuses.
- [ ] Job 9. Check front indicators.
- [ ] Job 10. Number plate lights.
- [ ] Job 11. Reversing and foglamps.
- [ ] Job 12. Clean lamp lenses.
- [ ] Job 13. Check horns.
- [ ] Job 14. Check windscreen wipers.
- [ ] Job 15. Windscreen washers.
- [ ] Job 16. Check tyres.
- [ ] Job 17. Check spare tyre.
- [ ] Job 18. Wash bodywork.
- [ ] Job 19. Touch-up paintwork.
- [ ] Job 20. Aerial/antenna.
- [ ] Job 21. Valet interior.
- [ ] Job 22. Improve visibility!
- [ ] Job 27. Pipes and hoses.
- [ ] Job 28. Check handbrake adjustment.
- [ ] Job 29. Door and tailgate seals.
- [ ] Job 30. Check windscreen.
- [ ] Job 31. Rear view mirrors.
- [ ] Job 32. Wash and wax the bodywork.
- [ ] Job 58. Check seat belts.
- [ ] Job 59. Renew wiper blades.
- [ ] Job 60. Locks and hinges.
- [ ] Job 61. Cable release mechanisms.
- [ ] Job 62. Check seats & seat belts.
- [ ] Job 63. Test Dampers.
- [ ] Job 64. Check/renew disc brake pads.
- [ ] Job 65. Check/adjust drum brakes shoes.
- [ ] Job 76. Toolkit and jack.
- [ ] Job 77. Lamp seals.
- [ ] Job 78. Alarm remote units.
- [ ] Job 79. Adjust headlights.
- [ ] Job 80. Check hub bearings.
- [ ] Job 81. Check steering and suspension.
- [ ] Job 82. Exhaust emissions.

36,000 miles - Around the Car

36,000 miles - Under the Car

First carry out all Jobs listed under earlier Service Intervals as applicable.

☐ Job 23. Clean mud traps.

☐ Job 33. Check exhaust system.

☐ Job 34. Check steering rack gaiters.

☐ Job 35. Track rod ends.

☐ Job 36. Check drive-shaft gaiters.

☐ Job 37. Grease points.

☐ Job 38. Inspect for leaks.

☐ Job 44. Change engine oil/oil filter.

☐ Job 45. Renew oil filter.

☐ Job 46. Spark plugs.

☐ Job 47. Distributor.

☐ Job 48. Ignition timing.

☐ Job 49. Accelerator controls.

☐ Job 50. Carburettor settings.

☐ Job 51. Check clutch adjustment.

☐ Job 52. Cooling system.

☐ Job 53. Coolant check.

☐ Job 54. Heater controls.

☐ Job 55. Check water pump.

☐ Job 56. Check automatic transmission fluid.

☐ Job 57. Check power steering fluid.

☐ Job 83. Inspect underside.

☐ Job 84. Clear drain holes.

☐ Job 85. Check gearbox oil.

☐ Job 86. Check rear axle oil.

☐ Job 87. Check transaxle oil.

☐ Job 88. Check telescopic dampers.

☐ Job 89. Check lever-arm dampers.

☐ Job 90. Clutch hydraulics.

☐ Job 98. Renew ATF.

Date serviced:..

Carried out by:...
Garage Stamp or signature:

Parts/Accessories purchased (date, parts,

source)...

....

....

....

....

....